ONE THOUSAND SHADES OF PINK

Stories of Personal Power over Destiny

Dr. Bernard Straile, DC

This book presents real stories from the author's holistic clinic about people regaining their health, naturally, by improving their epigenetic expression through precision energy medicine treatments and unique therapy strategies. Plus, some entertaining twists as people confront and resolve symptoms they have learned to live with.

The stories presented in this book are not intended as a substitute for the medical advice of physicians. The reader should regularly consult a physician in matters relating to his/her health, particularly with respect to any symptoms that may require diagnosis or medical attention. Always consult your doctor for your individual needs.

The methods described within this book are the author's personal thoughts and observations. They are not intended to be a definitive set of instructions for any energy method or treatment. You may discover there are other methods and materials to accomplish the same result.

To protect the privacy of certain individuals, the names and identifying details have been changed.

3rd edition

“Technology has a shadow side. It accounts for real progress in medicine, but has also hurt it in many ways, making it more impersonal, expensive and dangerous. The false belief that a safety net of sophisticated drugs and machines stretches below us, permitting risky or lazy lifestyle choices, has undermined our spirit of self-reliance.”

- Andrew Weil

Table of Contents

Foreword

By Nenah Sylver, PhD

This unusual book is the work of an unusual man. I met Bernard Straile at a conference on electro medicine that I sponsored in Phoenix of October 2016. It was immediately apparent to me that Dr. Straile was no ordinary chiropractor when he told me that he was the originator of the I.M.A.E.T. system. As I'd had the pleasure of working with the I.M.A.E.T. before I ever met the man, I knew instantly that I wanted to speak with him in depth because I had a million questions.

The I.M.A.E.T. system of healing, for people and animals, is difficult to explain to someone unfamiliar with the technology; but I'll try. Physically, it consists of software that can be installed on any computer, a harness that attaches to the body, a box that touches the subject, and some optional accessories for additional contact (such as a blanket for an animal). The computerized database contains thousands of frequencies representing various substances and parts of the body. The frequencies range from allergenic substances, emotional stressors, diseases and microbes to meridians, homeopathic remedies, Ayurvedic medicines, the spine, organs, glands, vitamins, minerals, herbs, and much more.

Think of the I.M.A.E.T. as an exhaustive database of just about everything that could go wrong with the body-mind system and unbalance it toward ill health—which suggests at least an equal number of corrections (or balances) to make the system right again, toward wholeness if not wellness. Corrections are made using the energy signatures of items in the database that the operator decides to use. Put another way, the machine is communicating with your body-mind system on the level of quantum energy.

Rather than thinking of energy healing as "new age," the product of would-be science fiction writers with too much time on their hands, understand that this way of healing has a foundation in physics. For over a century, we have known that humans receive, store and transmit electrical, magnetic, and electromagnetic fields. As everything in the universe has an energetic signature, it makes sense that imprinting corrective frequencies will alleviate or eliminate entirely the harmful effects of incorrect or destructive frequencies. Generally, this system of healing is far less invasive, and more effective, than drugs or surgery.

The I.M.A.E.T. was inspired, in part by a healing method developed by Dr. Devi Nambudripad called the Nambudripad Allergy Elimination Technique, or NAET. The word "allergy", as we commonly use the term, might seem confusing in this context; use the word "allergy" to mean "irritant," and it makes sense. Anything (whether inherently noxious or not) can act as an irritant to the body and cause it to overreact or behave abnormally.

Dr. Straile's SHOW method is to identify the substances that produce a pathological response and correct the body's response with bio-specific resonating frequencies. These treatments may target strengthening the body's abilities to detoxify or calming its overreaction. Herein lies the genius of the SHOW Method. In the pages that follow, you will learn how to connect the dots, or unearth the relationships between irritants ("allergens") and inflammation, which if left unchecked could lead to all kinds of disease and degenerative conditions. The important skill to develop for practitioners is in understanding how the body works, why it breaks down and its attempts to compensate for imbalances, and how its numerous physiological functions related to the thousands of allergens that persist in our environment unfold epigenetically. It's not always easy to connect the dots, even for practitioners with experience. This book offers a glimpse of many possible interrelationships between various bodily systems, organs, glands, meridians, even chromosomes and the stressors they encounter. Practitioners who use the I.M.A.E.T. will be interested in what Bernard Straile has to teach us. Clients who have benefited from the I.M.A.E.T. may be fascinated enough to further explore this modality. And if you don't have an I.M.A.E.T., you may want to own one—or at least consider how much this new model of thinking has to offer us.

We are energetic beings of vast potential. It's time to embrace modalities that deal with us on multidimensional levels.

"Energy is an inherent effort of everything multiplicity to become unity."

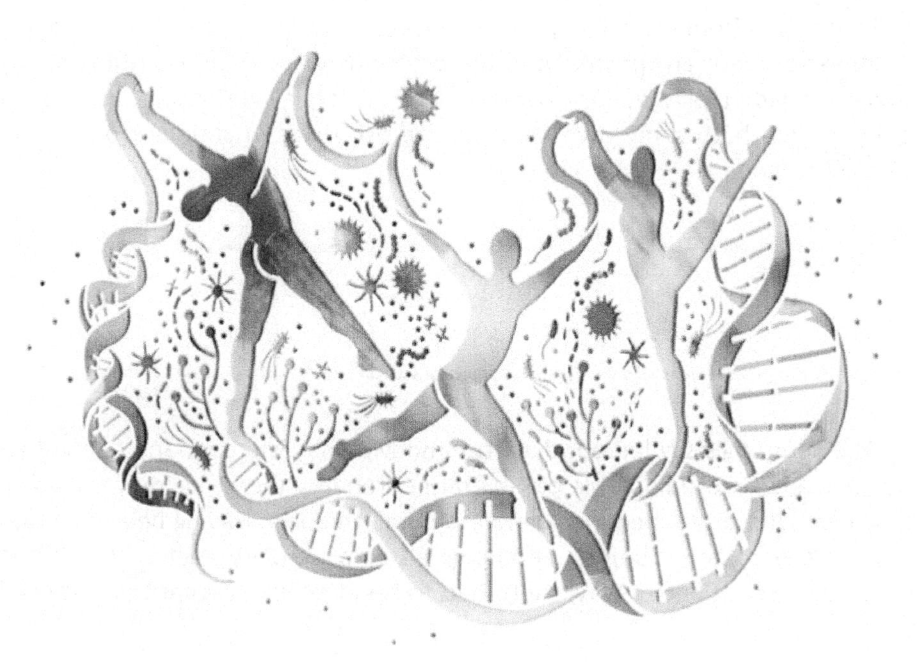

"To find yourself, think for yourself." - *Socrates*

Introduction

When I was a kid, my feet always hurt. The pain was bad enough for me to complain to my parents. My dad took me to the best orthopedist in town, who prescribed orthotics for me, because that's what they did back then. Sadly, if you complain about pain in your feet, that's what's still being done today.

The orthotics were very hard and uncomfortable, not to mention totally unnecessary, since I didn't have flat feet. It was essentially torture, which I endured for many years, paid for by health insurance.

As I grew into middle age and passed the 50-year mark, my feet still hurt! Unlike the pain from my childhood, my feet were starting to become numb, my foot muscles were **atrophying**, and the problems were even extending to my hands. I couldn't play guitar anymore. I couldn't play the piano anymore. I couldn't even button my own shirt. At age 50, I was in serious trouble and basically disabled.

Atrophy - body tissue or an organ wasting away, typically due to the degeneration of cells.

The neurologists ruled out diabetes and Multiple Sclerosis, and I ended up with a diagnosis of idiopathic peripheral neuropathy (nerve pain of unknown cause) and was prescribed medication to numb the pain. Having been told that "nothing can be done" before, and being a Doctor of Chiropractic, I knew that there had to be a better way; there had to be effective alternatives. I started investigating.

Acupuncture made the nerve pain worse, as did massage therapy. I did blood work and labs of all kinds. Everything was normal. Finally, I found out that I had food allergies – lots of them! The delayed onset type, also known as IgG. It turns out I was allergic to staple foods that I had been eating all my life— eggs, grains, dairy, peppers and peanuts.

Me, allergies? Why, I could drink gasoline, and nothing would happen to me! I was a young man, invincible, and a picture of health all my life as a motorcycle enthusiast, musician, pilot, doctor and entrepreneur. Except... my feet always hurt. I hadn't told anyone since my childhood, just as my father didn't tell anyone about his similar health issues. Maybe there was a connection between food allergies/sensitivities and my seemingly neurological issues? Maybe!

So, what can you do about allergies? Allergy specialists don't get rid of them; they just manage them with medication.

My investigations led me to NAET®, Nambudripad's Allergy Elimination Technique. NAET is a great natural technique to reduce and often entirely get rid of allergies. Through that NAET experience, realizing that I had a plethora of sensitivities to common stuff; feathers was another one, I had grown up as a child in feather bedding, I found that there was a gentle and energetic way to desensitize my body to this stuff. Later in that process, I discovered some other unpleasant things going on inside my body, including chronic viruses, spirochetes, fungi and parasites. These were all latent pathogens generating inflammation and disease inside my body, unbeknownst to me or my doctors.

I've had over 100 NAET treatments over the past 15 years, and while I am still very sensitive to the neurotoxins, we encounter every day, especially in food and drink, I am much, much better. My focus now is not just to improve my **metabolism** by eliminating all the allergy quirks within it, but to repair the

Metabolism - The complex of physical and chemical processes occurring within a living cell or organism that are necessary for the maintenance of life. In metabolism, some substances are broken down (such as foods) to yield energy for vital processes, while other substances (neurotransmitters, hormones, enzymes), also necessary for life, are synthesized(manufactured).

tissue damage that was caused over the past 50 years because of those quirks. The extent of the nerve damage, joint damage and accelerated aging was exacerbated by an inability of the healthcare system to recognize a functional problem, early on, preferably in childhood, and to respond to it energetically and functionally, instead of physically.

How did this misfortune befall me? What I now know is this:

It has to do with genetics (Thank You Dad) and **epigenetics**! Epigenetics I cannot blame on my parents. It's my responsibility to maintain a healthy epigenome by pursuing healthy lifestyle choices.

My father was on thyroid medication for low thyroid function all his adult life. However, I did not know this until I recently got involved in the coordination of my parents' healthcare, as they are turning elderly. My father also always was wearing special, expensive shoes. I now understand that his feet were very sensitive. Of course, he never mentioned anything to the family. As he grew older, I also noticed that the dexterity of his hands was deteriorating.

Epigenetics - Epigenetics refers to changes in gene expression – how genes behave, that do not involve changes in DNA sequence. These changes are thought to contribute to accelerated aging and various diseases.

However, he was very good at 'hiding' his shortcomings. He was determined to overcome his disabilities, but he was also aware of the limitations of the medical system in terms of any kind of constructive help with issues like his.

My personal epigenetic dysfunctions go back to my parents' genetics, plus the *toxic burden* from chemical use that was rampant while I was growing up in the 1950s and 60s. As a result, I also acquired significant epigenetic dysfunction.

- This could be expressed as cancer.
- This could be expressed as MS (multiple sclerosis).
- It could be expressed as asthma.
- For me, it is being expressed as peripheral neuropathy.

Thank you, God!

Having been a NAET practitioner myself for over 15 years and having treated thousands of patients through an energetic paradigm, I have identified multiple causes for many so-called idiopathic conditions. Idiopathic is the fancy term for health problems we don't know the cause of. These idiopathic most auto-immune conditions, are epigenetic dysfunctions that inflammation, manifesting in different tissues of the body. There are over different specialized tissues and depending on the individual's genetic constitution, the inflammatory symptoms manifest differently.

Did you know that each nutrient; vitamin, mineral, protein or fat requires a different set of genes to kick in, for these nutrients to be metabolized. From digestion to absorption to methylation, all is guided by genes. That brings us right away to the Immune System, which needs to be on guard for SIBO, Candida and other common intestinal infections.

In fact, epigenetic science confirms this idea. Every week, scientists announce that a new gene is discovered which is responsible for this or that pathology, a gene that turns on inappropriately or a gene that turns off when it shouldn't. This is often caused by a mutation of the gene, which makes it function less than optimally (as well as sometimes more than optimally).

The most common and simplest mutations are Single Nucleotide Polymorphisms (SNPs). Every individual has thousands of these SNPS. Nucleotides is the chemical term for alleles, the cross links of Adenine (A), Thymine (T), Cytosine (C) and Guanine (G).

In my clinical experience, as well as in my studies, I have found that we can influence

SNP–Single Nucleotide Polymorphism

The rungs of the DNA ladder are called Alleles. A switch-out of one of those alleles is called a SNP.

epigenetic function and genetic expression with specific energy treatments. Many energetic techniques have that potential. I know that the original NAET and my modern SHOW Method both have that power because they entail a significant level of metabolic detail. We check each nutritional component of s from combining ancient Eastern medical knowledge Western medical science (epigenetics) with different s. I have witnessed numerous times how the SHOW allergies permanently, detected chronic viruses, and focused n to engage in their rapid removal.

The SHOW Method (App 1) and NAET (App 2) are pragmatic, hands-on modalities that require some practitioner intuition, most often in the form of applied kinesiology, and MRT (Muscle Reflex Testing). This book illustrates some

---

SHOW Method – Straile's Holistic Options for Wellness, is an epigenetic healing method, which addresses metabolic stressors such as allergies and immune weakness at their epigenetic root cause, SNPs and genetic variants. It harmonizes genetic expression by resonating with the body's energy field through precision energetic feedback treatments.

---

of the clinical results from these techniques. I have developed a computer/software technology (IMAET System) parallel to the technique and method, which helps quickly, sort through the thousands of allergens, nutrients, chemicals, emotions, carcinogens, pathogens and microbes that one must consider or check. The SHOW Method -

- makes for smarter, more real time bio-informational health support.
- can help standardize treatments and make them more profoundly preventative.
- presents **epigenetic modulation** as a Quantum Biofeedback Technique, which can be applied in different, convenient therapeutic settings.
- Is designed to discover epigenetic dysfunction as energetic imbalances (allergies, infections, emotional trauma), long before these imbalances evolve into, and present as pathologies

__Epigenetic modulation__ – The precisely controlled regulation of gene expression plays an important role in normal cellular function, whereas abnormalities of gene expression can contribute to cancer and other diseases. Thus, the ability to selectively regulate gene expression is of tremendous importance, both as a basic research tool and as a potential therapeutic approach. (App 4)

The stories presented in this book are real-life cases from patients at my clinic, all of whom were treated with this energetic approach of informational medicine (SHOW Method), a new form of energy medicine, precision energy medicine.

The Quantum Biofeedback device utilized in the SHOW Method is the **IMAET**

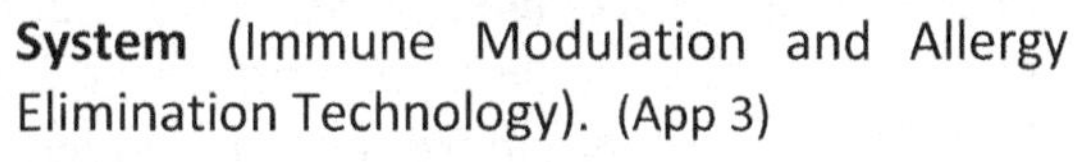

System (Immune Modulation and Allergy Elimination Technology). (App 3)

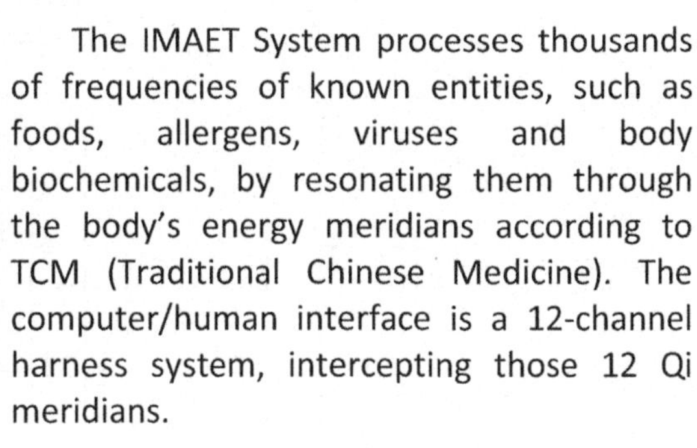

The IMAET System processes thousands of frequencies of known entities, such as foods, allergens, viruses and body biochemicals, by resonating them through the body's energy meridians according to TCM (Traditional Chinese Medicine). The computer/human interface is a 12-channel harness system, intercepting those 12 Qi meridians.

The IMAET software measures the reactivity signal of thousands of allergens, pathogens, toxins and emotions coming back from the body, ranks the imbalances by severity (of energetic reaction), and displays the results.

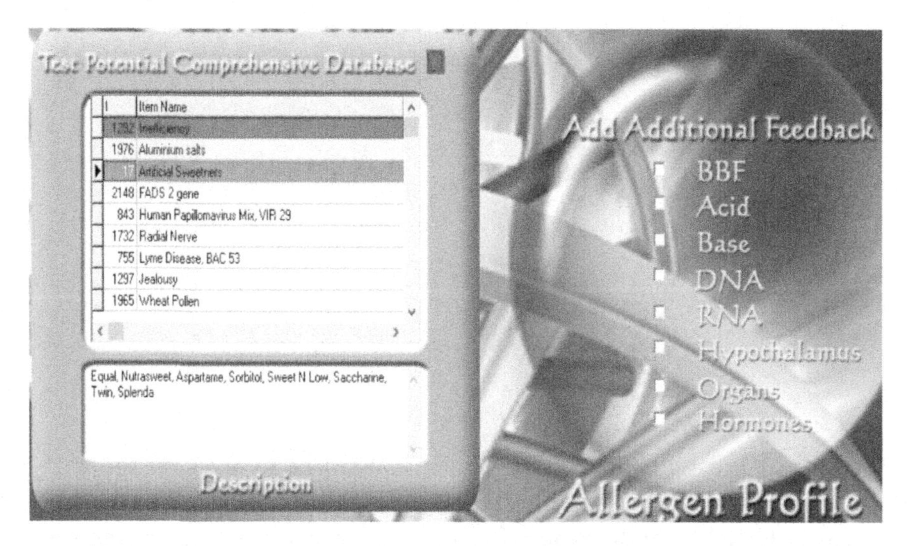

The scan results present incredibly important information about the (epigenetic) energy status of the body in real time. The practitioner can now put together a biofeedback protocol to modulate or harmonize selected imbalances for better epigenetic function. This is extremely exciting. Recognizing these **epigenetic stressors** that cause dysfunction can prevent some of the chronic illnesses that result from a lifetime of not knowing. How can we recognize **epigenetic stressors**?

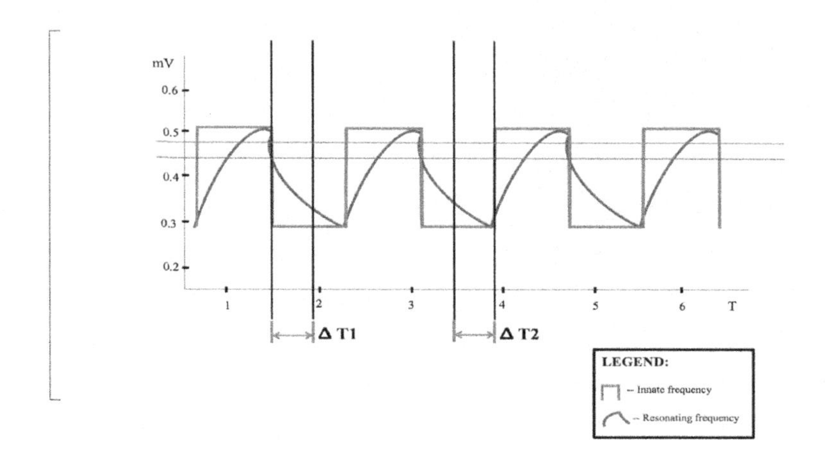

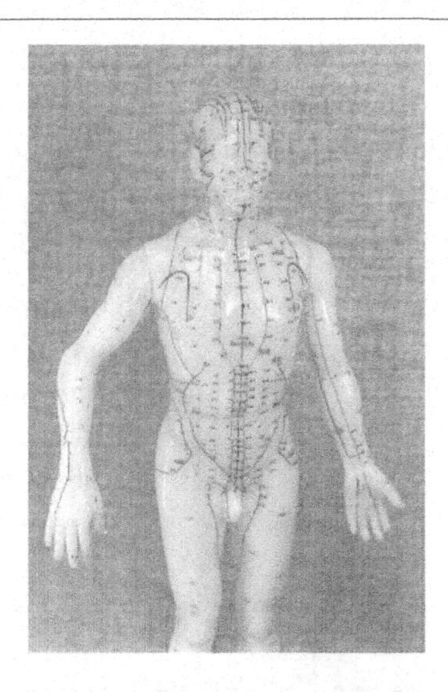

The SHOW Method recognizes the TCM model of energy meridians as the internet of the body through which all its cells communicate and connect. Through these communication channels, the cells coordinate survival from second to second. The Qi energy or Life Force flowing through these meridians, I analyze as data and information. This energy / information can reveal everything and anything going on in the body !

Since each cell has the entire DNA in its nucleus, this method allows us to:

a) to listen (scan) the body's metabolic, immune, detox etc. activities, it's cellular function.

b) to access the cells and their DNA and harmonize their function with a biofeedback treatment.

The SHOW Method allows us to interact and energetically communicate with the **genome,** our very essence, which is situated in the nucleus of every cell. Please know that our bodies consist of 100 trillion cells, so our DNA is present in the body 100 trillion times.

Genome - is an organism's complete set of genetic instructions. It is made up of DNA. The genome contains all information needed to build that organism, and allow it to grow, develop and maintain itself.

Childhood diseases are on the rise. Allergies, asthma, autism, depression, obesity... the list goes on and on. Our healthcare system is already non-sustainable, and it will almost certainly get worse. Healthcare must get smarter! We must include the energetic paradigm at its most advanced level.

A focus on real **prevention** is needed, not the mere early detection of pathology. We need information about the biochemical processes going on inside our bodies before ever a pathology appears. In real time, while one is at a doctor's office or any kind of health visit. Or, one can opt to do this at home as a self-help tool. A bit of STARTREK type of "tri-corder" action. This is not fiction any longer. It's here now and it needs to be integrated into our wellness care system. Probably even the healthcare system, particularly in Obstetrics and Pediatrics. To PREVENT Autism, Asthma, Alzheimer's and chronic illness.

Toddler receiving a SHOW Method biofeedback treatment related to his allergies and immune challenges. (8 channel head harness only)

This book presents real stories showing that smart prevention is possible now and that the results are profound and often surprising. The parallel component to building stronger, healthier humans, independent from drugs, is to foster a strong and healthy immune system. The notion that we can and should vaccinate against everything is ill conceived and dangerous. Furthermore, it is dangerous to our genome and therefore dangerous to our health. The present paradigm of chemical intervention damages the genome. Habitual pharmaceutical healthcare is dangerous to the health of future generations – our children and grandchildren.

It is important to recognize genetic predispositions by acknowledging symptoms to be red flags rather than just inconveniences and modulating those genetic predispositions before they become frank pathologies. It is imperative to maintain health, rather than wait for a disease to become life-threatening, and it is essential to intervene early in childhood before genetic core dispositions lead to a lifetime of tissue damage, chronic illness and suffering. It is now possible to provide people with these options, but the mainstream medical system cannot provide this service.

My purpose in writing this book is to show, through my own family's health history and a lifetime of continuous learning from my patients, that *now* is the perfect time to take charge of one's destiny, that your health is your responsibility, and that the pursuit of effective prevention through informational energy medicine is the path to solidifying that personal health and wellness.

The aim of this book is to create awareness of the importance of energetic factors within all life. This awareness will hopefully lead to a change in personal decisions about health maintenance, thus reducing suffering and daily pain caused by an ignorance of cause and effect within the medical system.

One egregious fall out from our drug driven healthcare system is the present opioid addiction crisis. Pain comes from inflammation and inflammation has metabolic causes as described earlier. Inflammation can and must be resolved systemically.

Systemic = System-wide: affecting or relating to a group or system (such as a body, economy, or market) as a whole, instead of its individual members or parts.

This book seeks to create awareness that prevention is possible in a methodical and precise manner and that it can be achieved now. It encourages readers to think about energetic patterns, which include cellular communication and our functional DNA (epigenetics) and let go of the monopoly of the rigid physical paradigm.

The change in thinking about what we need comes through our own experiences. And so, the change to a wellness paradigm with an energetic and informational focus will only come from the grassroots – **YOU.**

"Look deep into nature, and then you will understand everything better."

- Albert Einstein

Chapter 1 – Migraine Headaches

Caleb is a middle-aged professional in his 50s. Life is good; he is in good physical shape, exercises regularly and eats well. He even practices Yoga. Just one little problem, he experiences random migraine headaches, often triggered by bright lights. These migraines don't occur daily, about once a week and they are relieved by Excedrin. Caleb is referred to our office by his massage therapist. He would like to get rid of these migraines. So, off to work we go: Harmonizing his metabolism, utilizing the process I use with the SHOW Method. Finding and eliminating his allergies; food, airborne and environmental. As well as finding and getting rid of any chronic or latent infections.

The first set of treatments were:

- **Vitamin B Complex**
- **Salt**
- **Viruses** (common cold & flu)
- **Grains**
- **Yeast** (candida albicans, brewer's yeast, baker's yeast)
- **Tree Nuts**

We also addressed the airborne allergy of

- **Hay fever**

Hay fever is a mixture of summer grasses, ragweed, goldenrod and weeds.

Low and behold, after these seven SHOW Method treatments Caleb's migraines went away. He was impressed and very happy. Right away he referred his wife to address some of her health issues.

Pretty soon, Caleb and his wife took a summer trip to the Rocky Mountains and wouldn't you believe it, he had a migraine out there. I told him, this is not unusual and almost to be expected, that there are some allergens and bugs out there which we haven't discovered yet. So, let's find out what happened and treat it, by harmonizing the processing and breakdown of those allergens within his metabolism.

We ran an IMAET scan and did some kinesiology testing to prioritize the scan results. These are the issues that surfaced and the subsequent SHOW treatments we performed:

- **Reoviruses** (Reovirus infections occur frequently, but most are mild or subclinical. (NIH)
- **Vitamin B9** also known as **Folate**
- **Vitamin B 12**
- **MTHFR A1268C** (methylation gene related to Folate)

So far, Caleb's migraines are a thing of the past. That's very good not only for the pesky discomfort it saves Caleb from, but the improvements of his metabolism relating to B Vitamins as well as the new vigor of his Immune System. No longer does it allow as many latent viral infections, which are notorious for causing cancers. These improvements are for the rest of his life. The little relapse in the Rocky Mountains made us aware of his Folate and Vitamin B12 issue related to a MTHFR mutation (SNP). We were able to quickly harmonize and improve the function of that gene with the delivery of a SHOW Method biofeedback treatment. (more on the MTHFR gene and it's SNPs in the chapters ahead)

Conclusion:

1) One cannot give up at the first or second obstacle. This is a lifetime process, every day when you choose what to eat and drink; every time when you notice a health concern or symptom and you decide how to go about pursuing a resolution, you choose your destiny.

2) Every symptom should be looked at as a "red flag" of an underlying metabolic or epigenetic dysfunction. And the kind of energetic biofeedback described here, can successfully improve that innate function, one functional issue at the time.

Remember, everyone has thousands of SNPs and genetic variants, which can tilt your predispositions in a good way or just as often, a not so good way. What I am showing in these chapters is, that we can change our epigenetic expression in a good direction for better health, quality of life and longevity.

"Courage is the most important of all virtues, because without courage, you cannot practice any of the other virtues consistently." *- Maya Angelou*

Chapter 2 - Infertility

Infertility, an inability to conceive after having regular unprotected sex, usually over a period of more than 12 months can be devastating for couples ready to become parents. Studies have shown that just over 50% of cases are due to female problems, with the remaining balance caused either by sperm disorders or unidentified factors (Nordqvist, 2015). It is estimated that in the USA, approximately 10-15% of couples are dealing with infertility.

Diane, a woman in her late 30s, walked into our clinic one day and enquired about what we did and wanted more details on our energy treatments. After chatting with my staff for a while, they informed her that there was an upcoming public talk by Dr. Straile at the local library on "Lupus, how to heal yourself from it" and that she was more than welcome to attend. (The SHOW Method is a fundamental method, that follows the body's individual weaknesses. It can be applied to any health challenge.)

Diane is not the kind of woman to let grass grow under her feet, so she attended the lecture at the library (even though she did not have Lupus). Later, Diane would often come around to the Wellness Center, as she sensed that this kind of medicine could be something that would help her.

Diane was desperate to have a baby. She and her husband had been trying to conceive for several years and she was losing hope of ever having children. After the age of 35, infertility is defined as the inability to conceive naturally after six months and Diane had been trying for a lot longer than that. We decided to focus on Diane's health and prepare her body for pregnancy. Diane would do anything to have a child, swinging from the chandeliers if that's what it took! Fortunately, that wasn't necessary in her case.

Here is the testimonial she posted online after her successful pregnancy:

"Hello, my name is Diane and I had been trying for almost eight years to get pregnant. My husband and I had seen a fertility doctor whose only answer was 'unexplained infertility.' I did everything I could to have a baby. I had charted my cycle, used ovulation kits, tried different positions, etc. - but to no avail.

We didn't have the means for in vitro fertilization. Besides, I was multiple birth and how the drugs would affect the baby's developn age of 37, I had sadly resigned myself to not having children.

One day, instead of driving past The Total Wellness Center in Camillus, I decided to finally stop in, more out of curiosity than anything else.

I remember thinking, 'What have I got to lose?'

That simple decision has changed my life. First, there was Dr. Straile, who said that my body knows how to heal itself, but it needed someone who knew how to tap into (and support) its natural healing abilities. He cautioned me that natural approaches to health don't always work overnight and that I would need to make a long-term commitment to my health if I truly wanted to get pregnant. Together, we would have to slowly peel away all the accumulated issues that were preventing pregnancy.

I saw Dr. Straile once a week for seven months. Using the IMAET software and kinesiology, he determined what allergies were stressing my body. Many of these were either diminished or eradicated. He used chiropractic approaches to correct my physical structure. As my health got better and better, I had fewer and fewer colds because my immune system became stronger. I didn't even need my allergy medicine during ragweed season anymore.

My body needed many of the supplements found in Dr. Straile's natural pharmacy, including those for heartburn and morning sickness. And then, one day, out of the blue, I felt that I had conceived. Yes, you heard me right. I got pregnant!

I am happy to say that today my husband and I are the proud parents of a beautiful baby boy we named Johnny Alexander. Thank you Dr. Straile and everyone at the Total Wellness Center!"

Infertility is a complex condition that can have many contributing factors that may require medical or surgical intervention. Let's put it into perspective. The National Infertility Association states that young and fertile couples have a 15–20% probability of conceiving naturally per cycle. However, with IVF (in vitro fertilization), the success rate only increases to 20 – 35% per cycle. The American Society of Reproductive Medicine (ASRM) lists the average price of an IVF cycle in the U.S. to be $12,400, which can become extremely expensive if the first one doesn't take. When additional treatments are required, such as donor eggs and/or sperm or the transfer of frozen eggs, the costs can skyrocket into the tens of thousands of dollars per cycle.

nfertility drugs also wreak havoc on a woman's body. The American regnancy Association states that the side effects of these drugs include mood swings, depression, ovarian hyper-stimulation syndrome and the risk of multiple births, which is considered the greatest health risk associated with fertility treatment. Traditional fertility treatment is also dependent on a host of factors, such as age, weight, reproductive history and clinical diagnoses, yet even after all of this, up to 25% of infertile couples are classified as suffering from "unknown infertility."

Stress is also a factor that needs to be considered. Naturally, a woman who wants to get pregnant and is unable to do so is more likely to suffer from stress and depression. A recent Japanese study found that approximately 40% of women with infertility problems are clinically depressed or anxious even *before* being treated for infertility. Combined with the financial strains, is it any wonder that many women still fail to conceive?

Considering all these depressing factors, doesn't it make sense to treat the entire body and eliminate all stressors before going through the additional stress of infertility treatment? Working with your body, eliminating allergies, sensitivities and latent infections, releasing emotional trauma, and getting the right exercise is the best way to ensure a healthy and happy pregnancy – and child! Eliminating heritable allergies and dormant infections while harmonizing one's genetic expression makes the baby's genome less vulnerable to adverse reactions from vaccinations, antibiotics, food chemicals, and therefor issues such as Autism, Eczema, Asthma and a host of allergies.

Diane was anxious to become pregnant, but she had most of the "classic" food allergies, as well as many chronic and dormant infections. With patience and determination, we treated them with the SHOW Method over a 7 months period:

- **Grains & Gluten**
- **Vitamin B Complex**
- **Poultry layer** (egg white, egg yolk, chicken, feathers)
- **Shellfish, Fish**
- **Molds** (common varieties)
- **Vit K** plus common virus
- **Cystathionine synthase** (an enzyme related to the CBS gene)
- **Dairy & Calcium**

- **Viruses** (common flu and cold)
- **Nightshade vegetables and spices** (peppers)
- **Legumes** (dried beans and soy)
- **Vitamin C** and **Somatostatin**
- **Iron**
- **Yeasts** and **molds**
- **Minerals** and **dust**
- **Vitamin B Complex with Yeasts**
- **Vitamin C with Tree pollen**
- **Mucor (fungus), Astrovirus, Influenza Type A, Orthomyxovirus**
- **Parasites**
- **Xanthinoxidase** (an enzyme involved in uric acid detoxification)

While Diane was undergoing the more than 20 required treatments to eliminate her allergies and focus her immune system on dormant infections, I continually reminded her to have faith in the process and her body's ability to heal itself with the support of natural remedies. She needed to stay focused and look forward to having a healthy baby soon – emphasis on "HEALTHY!"

After a little over a year, all our hard work was rewarded. A beautiful 10-pound baby boy finally arrived, healthy as can be!

Fourteen months can feel like a long time and some women have had successful pregnancies in a much shorter period. Even so, Diane is a perfect example that identifying key epigenetic quirks, like allergies and sensitivities, as well as building up the immune system to clean up lingering infections, will deliver your desired result in a natural and sustainable way.

And, in Diane's case, she also delivered a HEALTHY baby who is much less prone to developing autism, asthma or allergies of his own. The mother, of course, is also much healthier (although temporarily a bit more sleep deprived). She can be a better parent, as she has more energy, is in better shape, and doesn't have to deal with the side effects of having her life-giving body polluted with chemicals and hormones but ignoring many inflammatory factors and latent infections.

The cost for two healthy and three happy people?

Approximately $1600 in treatments and $400 in natural remedies. Total cost: $2000 over 7 (plus) months.

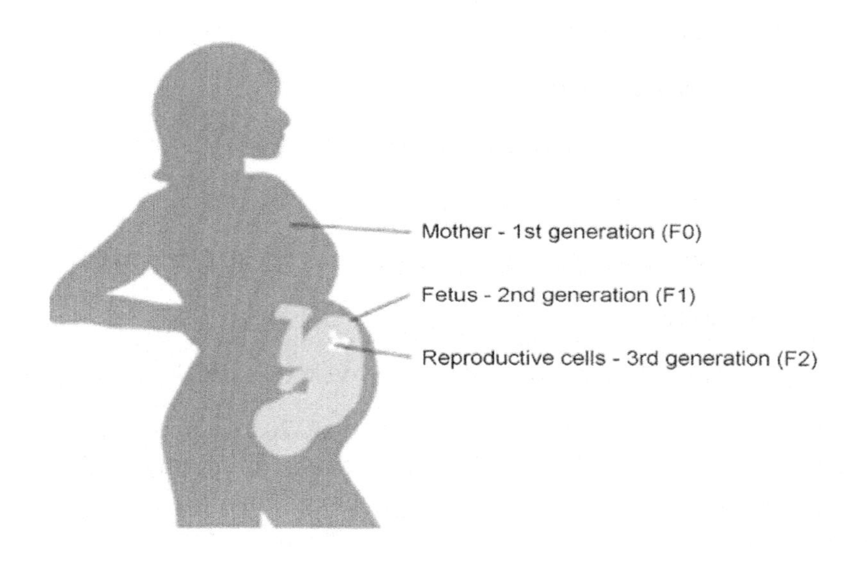

"It is health that is real wealth and not pieces of gold and silver."
- Mahatma Gandhi

Chapter 3 – Eczema

Belinda has four boys and their house is crazy enough to qualify for a reality show! As the director of the madness, like any mother of young children, Belinda was always on the edge of being overwhelmed, but she also had the additional stress of dealing with a wide range of health issues affecting her children that would drive a lesser mortal to their knees. However, Belinda gritted her teeth and went looking for answers to help her boys.

Depending on the day, four-year-old Oliver, who had been diagnosed with a "failure to thrive" (amongst other diagnoses) would be unresponsive, seemingly in a state of deep depression, only to emerge the next day severely anxious and agitated, working himself up into towering rages. This was accompanied by constant eczema, waxing and waning from moderate to severe, depending on the day. He also had various intestinal issues, ranging from cramping to projectile vomiting, which occurred daily. Remember, that is just one out of *four boys*... can you imagine?

Oliver's older brother, Harry, was one year older and suffered from severe eczema. Belinda reported that it had first appeared when he was three months old. His hyperactivity and ADD (Attention Deficit Disorder) kicked in at four years of age. Although Harry's diagnosis was eczema, he could have also been diagnosed on the autism spectrum.

Charlie was the oldest of the bunch at almost seven years old, and seemingly mellow compared to his younger siblings. His eczema was also quite mild. He avoided dairy products and, because of the constant emergencies with his younger brothers, he got the least amount of attention. He had many basic food allergies, but less severe.

The youngest of the family, at the point when they entered my practice, was Noah, three years of age, and the terror of the home, especially to his brothers! While he had all the classic food allergies, they seemed to be of less severity. Despite his brat status with his brothers, he was just a regular kid with allergies. The worst environmental issues for him were animal dander and hair, which would turn his already instigating personality more aggressive, leading to chaos, fighting and a deterioration of peace in the house.

By the time Belinda requested my help with her family's horrendous allergies and environmental sensitivities, she had already started working with an integrative allergist and the entire family was avoiding dairy, wheat and nuts. This took the edge off some of the most severe symptoms. Consuming these food groups would trigger anaphylactic reactions and frequent trips to the ER – just to liven things up a bit more. Therefore, the family (pre-NAET/SHOW treatments) was on a very restricted diet and jokingly told the story when Harry had turned an interesting shade of orange from eating too many carrots and drinking loads of carrot juice – the one food item they felt was not aggravating his symptoms.

With all those issues going on with her sons, it was easy to overlook Belinda, the mother of this small clan. She was clearly very concerned and stressed about her children and was searching for solutions for her sons' allergy symptoms. While treating her boys, however, and learning their stories, I noticed that Belinda also displayed the symptoms of allergies. Her sinuses were always congested, she had trouble breathing, and she seemed constantly fatigued. I suggested that we take care of her allergies as well. I just wanted to give her some relief from her own personal misery, since she was obviously struggling with her allergies. She finally agreed. I treated Belinda for all the basic food groups, just like her kids:

- **Poultry** (eggs, chicken, feathers)
- **Calcium & Milk**
- **Vitamin C**
- **Vitamin B Complex**
- **Sugars**

At that point in my career, I was using the NAET protocol (2), and was having a lot of success with allergy elimination in my clinic.

As luck would have it, Mom got pregnant again. Actually, she got pregnant three more times over the next five years. But, here's the kicker... There was one big difference between those younger boys and their older siblings: the youngsters hardly had any allergies. There was a significant drop in their sensitivity to all things. It was an amazing turnaround within the family! We all expected the same nightmare scenario to keep reappearing, as in the previous set of boys, but the problems disappeared! Of course, after boy number seven, we began teasing the family, "You're going for a whole football team now!" Alas, it was not in the stars, as the seventh boy, Jack, was the last.

This was one of the first times I could see clearly, right in front of my eyes, that changes in allergic conditions are heritable. There was no more doubt in my mind... ***Reducing and eliminating inflammation at the functional level, is heritable.*** *WOW!* The question is, what does that mean?

It means that these functional changes are occurring at the **epigenetic** level, or more broadly, at the ***cellular*** level. Allergies and autoimmune conditions are

Epigenetics - means "above" or "on top of" genetics. It refers to external modifications to DNA that turn genes "on" or "off." These modifications do not change the DNA sequence, but instead, they affect how cells "read" genes.

epigenetic dysfunctions.

These epigenetic changes can also be heritable, meaning that they are passed on from the parents to the next generation. Unfortunately, our children do not exclusively inherit our positive character traits, like blue eyes and beautiful smiles; they also inherit the health problems that we might have. We suspected that part already, given that certain allergies and autoimmune conditions, such as rheumatism, run in families. However, the fact that these inflammatory monsters could be turned off for the next generation was a great new discovery for me.

This revelation has very deep implications, and the knowledge needs to be broadly integrated into prenatal care. Why? First, to turn around the disturbing trend that over 50% of our kids are NOT healthy. We now have the tools to ensure that children born today do not have to go through the trauma and stress that their parents had to endure while fighting certain illnesses. We can, and should, stop this cycle before the next generation is even born.

A study published in JAMA pediatrics (September 2013 issue) noted that children suffering from food allergies cost families, and the United States as a whole, almost $25 billion each year. According to Allergy UK, the number of allergy sufferers is increasing, and approximately 40% of all people will have an allergic reaction at some time in their lives.

Most of these statistically recorded allergies are IgE-mediated. IgE **(Immunoglobulin E**) antibodies are only found in mammals, and it is speculated that these antibodies protect us from various pathogens, such as hookworms and other parasites that we try our best not to think about.

However, an even larger number of allergies are of the delayed onset variety, by as much as several days, and they are IgG-mediated; meaning that those antibodies only start fighting long after the food has been consumed. These kinds of hidden allergies are responsible for many inflammatory conditions, including eczema and many autoimmune conditions.

Immunoglobulins *- are protein molecules that contain antibodies. They are produced by the terminal cells of B-cell differentiation known as plasma cells. Immunoglobulins have important roles in acquired (humoral) immunity. They consist of 5 major classes: immunoglobulin G (IgG), A (IgA), M (IgM), D (IgD), and immunoglobulin E (IgE).*

Immunoglobulin G molecule (Medscape.com)

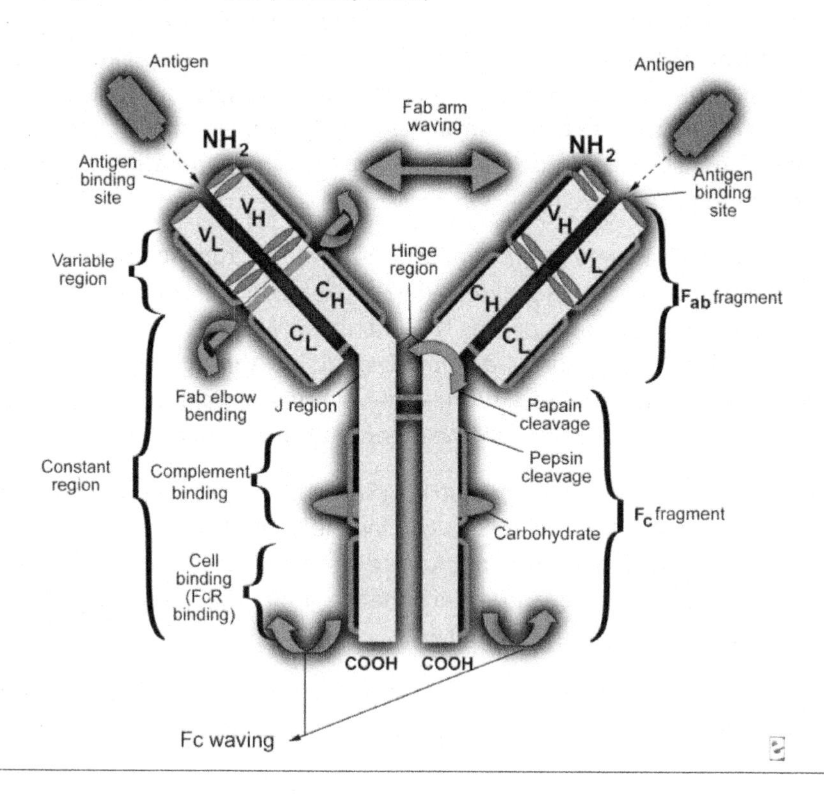

Due to the delayed onset, it is often difficult to precisely understand what is causing the reaction. However, when we do understand and discover what is causing this reaction, we can alleviate the suffering and ensure health, not only for that one person, but also for the generations that follow.

I treated the boys for all the basic food and airborne allergens in the SHOW Method.(see App. A). We had actually started out with the NAET protocol (App 2), which has a similar approach. All the major Vitamins, Proteins, Fats and Minerals.

And we treated several environmental items like

- lye (soap)
- chlorine and
- household cleaners.

Gradually the eczema reduced and eventually went away altogether. No more dietary restrictions, the ADD issues improved dramatically. Life went back to some kind of normal. Even Pizza, hot dogs and an occasional soda was a go.

Oliver turned out to be the toughest out of the bunch, and we had to visit several emotional issues and remove their energy blocking effect on his metabolic function. We even treated an "allergy" to two of his siblings. **Yes, Indeed, one can be allergic to a person.**

Oliver remains a sensitive fellow. When a new material, such as blow-in insulation is introduced in their house, he can develop an eczema type of response. He then comes to the office with a sample of the offending stuff and we desensitize him to it and then he is ok.

It's been a real privilege to work with this family. I learned so much from them, about the heritability of the SHOW Method treatments and **epigenetic harmonization treatments (EHT)**. How these issues run in families and yet, still remain distinctly individual.

Epigenetic Harmonization Treatments (EHT) – energetic biofeedback treatments (ASR Biofeedback) resonating with specific genomic components, from body biochemicals and proteins to receptors and genes.

"A man who refuses light will remain in the darkness, even by the side of light!" - *Mehmet Murat ildan*

Chapter 4 - Night Blindness

While I was working with Belinda and learning about how the elimination of allergies can be passed along from one generation to the next, we made another startling discovery.

We were reducing Belinda's many allergies, slowly and meticulously, one by one, following the SHOW Method (see App 1). This included all the common food groups, vitamins, minerals, proteins and fats, and we were making good progress with her symptoms of congested sinuses, rashes and fatigue. One day, Belinda asked me to check onions, as they always seemed to bother her. Intestinally by causing gas and especially burning her eyes and making them teary when cutting onions.

Sure enough, onion reacted with **MRT** (Muscle Reflex Testing) or **kinesiology.**

MRT – Muscle Reflex Testing: man testing woman (arm test), also known as Applied Kinesiology.

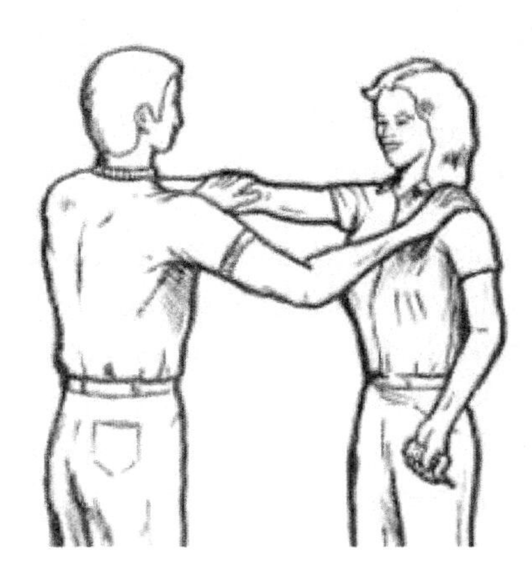

So, onions became the main treatment focus that day. I zeroed in on:

- **ONION**

and the combinations related to the digestion of onions. This was a routine treatment, centered on digestive co-factors, such as:

digestive enzymes (represented by Base), brain focus (represented by Hypothalamus) and epigenetic focus (represented by DNA).

Onions are found in most meals, garnishes and soups, so it is important to investigate whether they are an allergen. We finished the treatment and scheduled a follow-up appointment in a few weeks. Nothing out of the ordinary.

The next time I saw Belinda, she was beside herself with happiness. She said, "Dr. Straile, right after you treated me for onion last time, the very next day my night blindness was gone. Just like that. I can drive at night again without a problem."

I was astounded. She had never told me that she suffered from night blindness. I had no idea.

Just another beautiful day in the neighborhood.

Kinesiology – a form of muscle reflex testing or MRT. Based on the concept of internal energy, as found in traditional Chinese medicine, muscle testing is a noninvasive way of evaluating the body's imbalances and assessing its needs. It involves testing the body's responses when applying slight pressure to a large muscle, to provide information on energy blockages, the functioning of the organs, nutritional deficiencies, and food sensitivities, among other things. It can also be used to test the body's responses to herbs and other remedies.

Belinda was already dealing with a number of serious issues at the time, which is why she never told me about the night blindness, nor put it in her history questionnaire. Although she never mentioned the issue, it must have been hard to deal with. Due to all the medical emergencies with her children, she must have been even more anxious than usual when she had to go out at night. Night blindness can affect people in many ways. In Belinda's case, it prevented her from driving her children to an emergency room at night on her own. She would have been hesitant to go out after dark. I later learned that even being at home in the dark was uncomfortable. When she discovered that her night blindness was gone, everyone was delighted.

Night blindness can sometimes be treated with conventional medicine. It can also be caused by cataracts, near sightedness or a deficiency of Vitamin A. In other cases, night blindness can be caused by diabetes. However, Belinda did not have any of these conditions, and conventional medicine hadn't helped at all.

I'm still not sure which component caused the night blindness. Onions are high in a particularly strong sulfur compound, allyl propyl di-sulphide. That is what makes you cry when you peel onions. Peeling the onion releases a fine spray of this biochemical, which gets into your eyes and causes the tearful reaction.

I had already treated Belinda for a Vitamin A allergy a few months earlier. In the developed world, it's safe to say that most Vitamin A deficiencies are caused by Vitamin A allergies or **metabolic errors** (from SNPs) in the digestion and activation of Vitamin A and not from limited food varieties.

Metabolic errors *- genetic (inherited) disorders in which the body cannot properly turn food into energy. The disorders are usually caused by defects in specific proteins (enzymes) that help break down (metabolize) parts of foods, such as Vitamin A.*

Leaky Gut *- a condition in which the lining of the small intestine becomes damaged, causing undigested food particles, toxic waste products and bacteria to "leak" through the intestines and flood the blood stream causing allergic reactions.*

Outside of the "**leaky gut**" phenomena and true toxicity, most allergies, in my clinical experience, fall under this category of metabolic errors within the genome.

A "leaky gut" is generally caused by intestinal candida or fungal overgrowth, which crowds out the beneficial bacteria and prevents it from doing its job. The beneficial gut bacteria actively absorb nutrients for us, while the fungus leaks undigested food particles into the bloodstream. And these "food particles", are not nutrients, and activate the immune system, which triggers major inflammation. This inflammation triggers symptoms like bloating, IBS (Irritable Bowel Syndrome), migraines and pain anywhere in the body, including the back/spine and any of the many joints in the body.

An example of toxicity versus allergy is alcohol. Anyone can develop toxic alcohol levels simply by drinking too much, which can even lead to a coma. However, a person that is allergic to alcohol will, upon the consumption of alcohol, experience a personality change, becoming aggressive or depressed, for example. These people are also much more prone to alcohol addiction.

Belinda's leaky gut and candida issues were resolved much earlier in her treatment protocol. The night blindness was caused by an epigenetic glitch in her DNA related to the processing of onions in her gut.

Onions are a powerhouse of goodness. Make sure your body can process them properly !

Bioactive products found in Onion (Allium cepa)
Pharmacology:
quercetin, fructose, quercetin-3-glucoside, isorhamnetin-4-glucoside, xylose, galactose, glucose, mannose, organosulfur compounds, allylsulfides, flavonoids, flavenols, S-alk(en)yl cysteine sulfoxides, cycloalliin, selenium, thiosulfinates, and sulfur and seleno compounds.
Effects of onion:
Antibiotic, Anticancer, Antidiabetic, Antimutagenic, Antihypercholesterolemia, Cardiovascular. (App 15)

"The most beautiful experience we can have is the mysterious. It is the fundamental emotion that stands at the cradle of true art and true science."

- *Albert Einstein, The World As I See It*

Chapter 5 - Hashimoto's Thyroiditis

Colleen's 16-year-old nephew, Chris, had a summer landscaping job. One day while clearing weeds, he inadvertently grabbed and pulled on some poison ivy with his bare hands. His hands became raw within hours and the inflammation and rash began spreading across his body. The pain was excruciating, and he needed emergency care. Luckily, some relatives were chiropractic patients here at the clinic and knew that we also dealt with allergies. They made an urgent appointment and Chris came in for the consultation. To his family's relief, the SHOW treatment provided quick and effective relief from his nasty symptoms.

Good news travels fast – very quickly, the whole extended family knew of Chris's experience. Colleen began wondering if her Hashimoto's might also be caused by allergies and whether it would be possible to reverse the symptoms. Colleen had been diagnosed two years earlier with Hashimoto's, bilateral large nodules in the thyroid gland and a goiter.

The butterfly-shaped thyroid Gland sits below the Adam's apple (larynx)

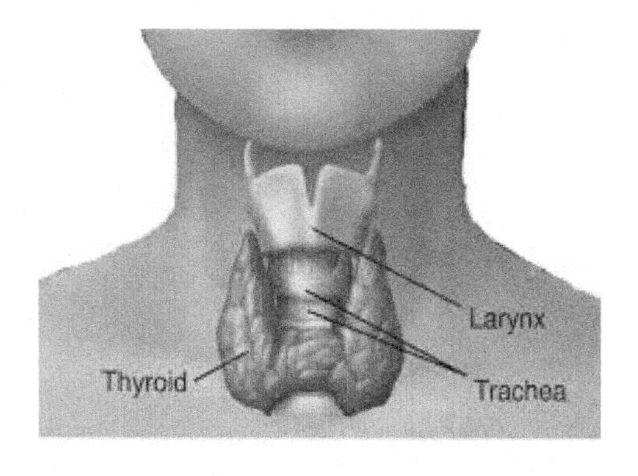

Bilateral *– on both sides.*

Hashimoto's is a disease where the immune system attacks the thyroid gland. The symptoms of an inactive thyroid are extremely unpleasant – sluggishness, fatigue, dry skin and constipation.

The endocrinologist strongly advised her to have the entire thyroid removed and put her on 125 mg of Synthroid. At the time, Colleen did some research on the Internet and was not convinced that removing the thyroid (thyroidectomy) was the solution. She resisted the radical surgery and two years later, when she arrived at my clinic, her thyroid was swollen and non-functional, but still intact.

We did blood tests which showed her CBC (Complete Blood Count) was normal and her **TSH** (Thyroid Stimulating Hormone) level had been stabilized with medication (Synthroid), but her Vitamin D levels were moderately low.

TSH – Thyroid Stimulating Hormone. Secreted by the pituitary gland to stimulate production of thyroid hormone (T 4) by the thyroid gland.

I started treating her metabolic dysfunctions and food allergies with the SHOW Method, as they came up in priority through IMAET scanning and MRT testing:

- **Eggs**
- **Vitamin B complex** and **grains**

  (This group of nutrients we had to treat and clear twice.)
- **Legumes, including peanuts**
- **Vitamin C**
- **Wheat** and **gliadin**
- **Nightshades**
- **Fats**
- **Calcium and milk**
- **Yeast and mold**

- **Minerals**
- **Sugars and milk**
- **Iodine**
- **Vitamin B complex** and **animal dander**
- **Iron and meat**
- **Vitamin A**
- **Food coloring and additives**
- **Salt**
- **Feathers**
- **Tree nuts**

The entire treatment protocol was spread out over three years, because Colleen wasn't always focused on the treatments as much as she should have been. The same progress could have been accomplished in less than a year. Nevertheless, after the first treatment episode, over the course of 10 months (about seven or eight treatments), her TSH was low and her T4 was above normal, so her endocrinologist reduced her thyroid medicine from 125 mg to 100 mg per day. The ultrasound also showed that her goiter had begun shrinking, and that her nodules were drying up. We were obviously making progress!

After another year of about 12 sessions, an ultrasound examination of the thyroid showed that the goiter and swelling were gone, while the nodules were completely gone on one side and sharply reduced on the other. Her blood work showed overmedication with Synthroid, so the endocrinologist further reduced the dosage of Synthroid from 100 down to 50 mg per day.

Today, Colleen is waiting for her tax refund before coming in for a few more treatments. She now breaks the 50 mg tablet in half, bringing the dosage of Synthroid down to 25 mgs per day, and has more energy now than she's had all her life. Her endocrinologist told her that "People don't ever get better with this condition." He was intrigued and asked her what she was doing, so Colleen told him about our treatments. He asked for my name and phone number and said he was interested in referring other patients to me. Needless to say – I never heard a word from the endocrinologist!

Luckily, Colleen resisted conventional wisdom and we were able to rescue her thyroid and bring it back to health. As it turns out, there was nothing wrong (as such) with her thyroid gland. It was her metabolic errors and allergies that had generated enough inflammation to produce an autoimmune condition

Gene expression - is the process by which the instructions in our DNA are converted into a functional product, such as a protein (enzymes, neurotransmitters, hormones).

(Hashimoto's). Her journey to real health continues for her and her family. This kind of preventative and restorative healthcare based on energetic analysis, enables us to "read the body" and communicate at the cellular level and change **genetic expression**. In return that allows us to mitigate and eliminate many inflammatory conditions by harmonizing genetic expression and completely alter the course of a life. For the better.

Update at the publishing of the 3rd edition of this book:

Colleen is now off Thyroid meds all together, but her blood work is still marginally high for TSH and marginally low for T4 (Thyroid Hormone). She feels better than ever, but her MD keeps pressuring Colleen to go back on Thyroid medication.

Finally, one fine day, EBV came up in a routine scan during an appointment.

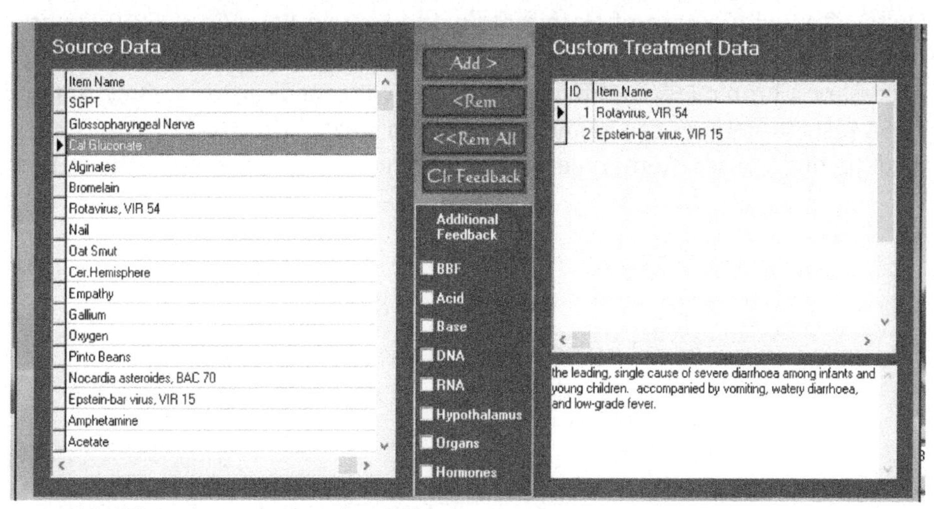

IMAET scan result showing EBV

Making sure, I checked Colleen with a vial for Epstein Barr Virus (EBV) and low and behold her body reacted to that test vial. Why I didn't recognize this important chronic infection earlier in one of the IMAET scans, I don't know. It's all about AWARENESS.

Since then, I have had numerous cases of Hashimoto's come through my clinic, all of which had EBV involvement. I now routinely check for EBV early on in the treatment protocol, whether it shows up in a scan or not.

Conclusion: One learns every day about the energetic realities of LIFE. They are complex and numerous. The good news – epigenetic science and bio-energetic science are confirming all of my clinical findings parallel and at the same time. These are really exciting times for the advancement of energy medicine and its application for 'changing epigenetic expression'.

Epstein-Barr virus (EBV) *- is a prevalent human herpesvirus affecting over 90% of the adult population worldwide. Most individuals harbor EBV asymptomatically as lifelong infections.*

Quite often with a case of Hashimoto's, the Epstein Barr Virus (EBV) is part of the problem or one of the triggers. Then, an immune treatment for that virus is necessary. Chronic EBV is difficult to detect with medical tests. Only Antibody ELISA tests sometimes can confirm it. But then what?! The IMAET System is good at detecting viruses. Sometimes sooner, sometimes later, due to the extreme

---

In the case of chronic EBV infection one needs to repeat an immune treatment multiple times over up to several months, to keep the immune system focused on this task of eliminating the virus 100%.

---

volume of biochemical activity in a human body.

I treated Colleen 6 times for

- EBV with combinations RNA, DNA, Hypothalamus

And even now, when Colleen comes in for a concern or a check-up, I test manually (with a vial and MRT) for EBV, to make sure it is not trying to make a comeback.

EBV causes all kinds of problems including Fibromyalgia and Chronic Fatigue, just to name a few. Chronic EBV has been linked to certain Lymphomas. And I am discovering chronic Lyme recently in my clinic potentially being part of the drivers of bladder and kidney cancers.

In Coleen's case, EBV was discovered a bit late, however, remember, we have to build up the Immune System to be able to tackle these infections by eliminating many common food allergies. Why? Because the Immune System needs the nutrients for its proper function. If all "hands are on deck", the Immune System is powerful beyond comprehension.

Hashimoto's is a classic example of how chronic infections can cause serious epigenetic changes leading to auto-immune diseases and even cancer. Luckily, we can change epigenetic expression, if we become aware of "the facts on the ground". Those facts can often very conveniently be realized energetically. And, as it turns out, our Immune System communicates energetically with the environment it has to deal with.

"The importance of breathing need hardly be stressed. It provides the oxygen for the metabolic processes; literally it supports the fires of life. But breath as "pneuma" is also the spirit or soul. We live in an ocean of air like fish in a body of water. By our breathing, we are attuned to our atmosphere. If we inhibit our breathing, we isolate ourselves from the medium in which we exist. In all Oriental and mystic philosophies, the breath holds the secret to the highest bliss. That is why breathing is the dominant factor in the practice of Yoga.

- Alexander Lowen, The Voice of the body

Chapter 6 – Asthma in a Young Man

A 23-year-old man was referred to me by his counselor. Jimmy had asthma, anxiety and a low sex drive. He associated the low sex drive with his being given Adderall throughout his school years for his so- called ADD (attention deficit disorder). He associated the asthma with his environmental allergies and sensitivities. This is what ultimately brought him to my clinic.

And so, we began to work on the issues which presented:

- Treatment #1 - **parasites**
- Treatment #2 - **Vitamin B complex**
- Treatment #3 - **MTHFR mutation** with **Vitamin B12** and **Folate.**

After these initial three treatments, he reported better breathing when running and jogging.

- **Calcium and dairy**

plus, a common flu virus were treatment #4.

MTHFR is a gene that provides instructions for making an enzyme called methylenetetrahydrofolate reductase. This enzyme is necessary for an important metabolic process called methylation. It is this process that converts folate (Vitamin B 9) into an active form of Vitamin B 9 which the cells then can metabolize.

Jimmy reported continuing improvement in the breathing aspect of his condition. During this part of the treatment protocol, we were supporting his adrenals with Desiccated Adrenals, a glandular product from Standard Process (App 5).

- **Vitamin C and tree pollen**

  were treatment # 5.
- **The poultry layer (eggs, chicken, feathers)**

  and more viruses were treatment # 6.
- **MSG (monosodium glutamate), fluoride,** and common **Staph and Strep bacteria**

  were treatment # 7.

Since Jimmy was quite young and healthy, we could often treat two groups of issues in one treatment. A metabolic issue, like a food allergy, and an immune condition, such as a viral or bacterial infection. His infections were usually latent, chronic or dormant, as they often are.

Jimmy's moods were still unpredictable. Emotionally, he was not yet stable, but his asthma was improving rapidly. We moved on to:

- **Sugars and pollen**

  in treatment #8
- **H-pylori** (a bacterium usually affecting the stomach lining) **and more viruses** with a combination of the **CBS gene**

  in treatment # 9.

---

*CBS - (**cystathionine beta synthase**) provides instructions for making an enzyme called cystathionine beta-synthase. This enzyme acts in a chemical pathway (Transsulfuration and Glutathionine Synthesis) and is responsible for using vitamin B6 to convert building block of proteins (amino acid) called homocysteine and serine to a molecule called cystathionine.*

---

o **Yeasts** combined with **Vitamin B complex**

were treatment #10.

Therapeutically we continued with the layer of:

o **grains, wheat, gluten, gliadin** and **pinene** (a phenol),

and more immune treatments:

o **chronic viruses.**

Through the course of treatments, it became apparent that Jimmy had many latent infections, which required a strong Immune System to clear them out, and that, in return, requires a well-functioning metabolism, to supply the immune system with required substrates (such as nutrients).

***Phenols** – phytochemicals that are present in food dyes, artificial flavors, preservatives and in highly colored fruits and vegetables, in bioflavonoids, and in carotenoids (carotene, lutein, lycopene, xanthophyll, and zeaxanthin). **Almost all foods have phenols**, but in varying amounts.*

I put Jimmy on AF-Betafood from Standard Process to stimulate bile flow and to help the liver dump its detoxification byproducts into the bile. Info on AF-Betafood (App 6)

We also completed treatments for:

o **Iron** and **molds,**

which were followed by a layer of legumes:

o **beans** and **peanuts.**

Biliary System:

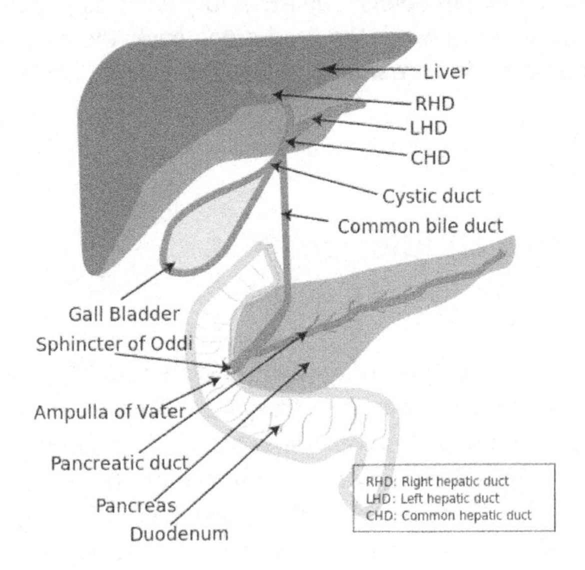

After 12 treatments, this young man is an entirely different person. He has no more asthma issues and can exercise without breathing difficulties, which greatly reduces his anxieties. His mood is consistently more upbeat, so he can go out and do the things that other 23-year-olds do, which require plenty of energy!

Jimmy's case of asthma was a moderate one. He was not using an inhaler but was aware of the fact that pharmaceuticals and environmental toxins troubled his body.

His consciousness led him to pursue natural alternatives and within twelve SHOW Method treatments, he was over 90% improved and ready to enjoy life without taking medications every day!

"With each breath, a wave can be seen to ascend and descend through the body. The inspiratory wave begins deep in the abdomen with a backward movement of the pelvis. This allows the belly to expand outward. The wave then moves upward as the rest of the body expands. The head moves very slightly forward to suck in the air while the nostrils dilate, or the mouth opens. The expiratory wave begins in the upper part of the body and moves downward: the head drops back, the chest and abdomen collapse, and the pelvis rocks forward." - *Alexander Lowen, The Voice of the Body*

Chapter 7 – Asthma in a Middle-aged Man

Bill is an established farmer who has suffered from asthma all his life. It prevented him from playing lacrosse in college, a true passion of his, and held him back in many other ways, notably in his younger years. Inhalers were a part of his everyday life. When he entered our practice at the age of 50, he was not feeling well, couldn't sleep, and complained about blurred vision, excessive appetite, nerve pain, wheezing and depression. He had also struggled with learning disabilities his entire life. However, what really brought him to us was the fact that he was constantly getting sick. He was on antibiotics all the time, usually once a month during the winter. It had begun to interfere with his ability to run the farm. His hope was that we could ease his predicament, never thinking or expecting that anything could be done about his asthma. He had lived with asthma all his life, but things had recently started to spin out of control.

One synergistic aspect in this case was that Bill was self-insured through the farm and his deductible was $10,000. However, I was astounded by the bills he had received from his allergist. Just to get the prescription renewed for his inhalers, he had to pay $275 for a specialist visit. It would cost him less than $10,000 in the first year to receive intense treatment and counsel at our clinic but be actually healed in the process.

We started working on his condition right away:

First, we harmonized his

- **Vitamin B (complex)** metabolism.

For the second treatment, we did the same with:

- **poultry,** which includes egg whites, the most basic protein in the food chain, egg yolk and chicken.

For the third treatment, we began to employ his newly empowered immune system and focused on

- **common flu and cold viruses**

that were active in his body but hadn't been touched by the barrage of antibiotics he had received over the years. Nutritionally, we supported his kidneys and immune system.

Treatment #4 –

- **Starch and yeast/candida**

Yeast includes intestinal candida, of which he had a serious case, due to his frequent use of antibiotics.

Treatment #5

- **Sugars and yeast**

The intestinal candida condition required special attention to resolve.

We initially supported his system with antifungals, such as oregano oil, to assist the immune system in killing off the fungus, and then followed up with probiotics to re-inoculate his intestinal flora with beneficial bacteria and allow him to absorb the nutrients he so desperately needed.

Treatment #6

- **Grains and B Vitamins**

His breathing gradually improved, and he didn't need his inhaler as frequently. He also started feeling a bit better, after only six weeks of treatments.

Next, we harnessed his budding immune system to handle some of the most common bacterial pathogens, namely:

- **Strep and Staph**.

Various other chronic bacterial infections had to be dealt with in the same way, through a standard SHOW Method treatment.

The immune system is responsible, amongst other things, for tackling any bacteria, but it's a numbers game. Once the immune system is overwhelmed, either by not being aware of an infection brewing in the body or by the person simply not actively doing anything to support their immune system, antibiotics can be a lifesaver. After this brief period of treatments, Bill never had to go back on antibiotics again. At the time of writing this book, it has been 10 years since he first entered my practice.

During this little series of immune treatments, we also did some emotional clearings. These emotional blockages became apparent through his resistance to clearing his egg white allergy. Emotions like impatience and financial concerns had to be cleared, in conjunction with his body's opposition to egg whites. Egg white does represent the simplest and most basic protein in food. Emotional trauma can block certain biochemical processes (Egg White is a common one) and thus cause inflammation and pain.

We continued working on bacteria of all kinds, as well as different types of molds and various phenols. All these treatments were tailored towards Bill being able to metabolically process these important items properly, without generating inflammation. This metabolic process requires certain enzymes to be expressed at the epigenetic level, so they can work to process these common **antigens** and pathogens.

***Antigens** - are the little invaders that enter the body and trigger the immune system. They come in all different shapes and sizes. Antigens are mainly microbes such as bacteria, parasites, and fungi. They can also come from the environment, such as viruses, chemicals, pollen, and more. Each antigen may cause infection to the body. There are some antigens that seem harmless but still cause the immune system to respond, like pollen for example. Then they are called allergens.*

This enzymatic process operates our metabolism and dictates our survival. Whether it's activating a vitamin, breaking down a protein to assimilate its amino acids, or making an immune factor to prepare an assault on a virus, our lives depend on these enzymes!

Treatment #12 was for:

- **tree nuts, a layer of vegetable oils, proteins and lectins.**

Lectins - carbohydrate-binding proteins present in most plants, especially seeds and tubers like cereals, potatoes, and beans. They are toxic and thought to protect the plants from being eaten.

I also discovered a serious Vitamin D deficiency through kinesiology testing (MRT). We addressed it with a dosage of 5000 I.U. Vitamin D3 per day for several months.

Five months into the treatment regimen, Bill was visiting us once a week when his work schedule allowed. He was doing significantly better in all aspects of his life.

His breathing had drastically improved and there was much less wheezing, but he still needed his inhaler from time to time, mostly while working on the farm. He was intermittently waking up at 1:30am, and finding it hard to get back to sleep, so his sleep disturbances also had to be addressed.

We started adding to the treatment regimen some airborne allergens, including:

- **tree pollen, pollen,**
- **grasses,**
- **wood,**
- **dust,**
- **insecticides,**
- **pesticides,**
- **weed killers**
- **animal dander**.

Yes, it appeared as though Bill was allergic to *everything*. One unforgettable epiphany occurred when I treated him for

- **Agent Orange**.

It had come up twice before in the IMAET scan in May, and so I double-checked the allergen manually through a vial, with MRT (kinesiology muscle testing). Bill's body reacted to the Agent Orange vial and I told him that Agent Orange was part of his treatment today, although it didn't make any sense, since Agent Orange was no longer in use (as far as I knew). So, I treated him for it. He went on to tell me that he had recently been spraying weed killer on his newly plowed and seeded fields, and that Agent Orange was in the formula.

During the Vietnam War, US military forces sprayed millions of gallons of herbicides (plant-killing chemicals) on land in Vietnam, Laos, and other nearby areas to remove forest cover, destroy crops, and clear vegetation from the perimeters of US bases. This effort, known as Operation Ranch Hand, lasted from 1962 to 1971. Different mixes of herbicides were used, but most were mixtures of two chemicals that were phenoxy herbicides:

- *2,4-dichlorophenoxyacetic acid (2,4-D)*
- *2,4,5-trichlorophenoxyacetic acid (2,4,5-T)*

Each mixture was shipped in a chemical drum marked with an identifying colored stripe. The most widely used mixture contained equal parts 2,4-D and 2,4,5-T. Because this herbicide came in drums with orange stripes, it was called Agent Orange.

I found it hard to believe that Agent Orange was commonly used in agriculture today, so I traveled to the farm to check for myself. There it was: 34% of the weed killer formula, which farmers across the country spray on their fields by the tons in the spring after plowing their fields, was composed of Agent Orange. In other words, besides the farmers and farmhands handling that material and being exposed to it, the wind also carries away some of that toxic concoction and WE, our children, and everyone else living near rural areas are breathing it in. Airborne Agent Orange and weed killers can cause sore throats, headaches and wheezing. The rest of that Agent Orange ends up on our food and in the groundwater.

Every so often, we had to reinforce Bill's viral and bacterial immune function, as well as treat various molds when they appeared on the IMAET scans. One year after entering my practice, and after receiving about 30 treatments, Bill only carried his rescue inhaler as an intervention for occasional flare-ups, triggered by inhalants that he was exposed to on the farm. At times, however, he would wake up at 4am, still unable to go back to sleep.

We continued into the second year with a less intense schedule, meeting once every two weeks when his schedule allowed.

- **Soy and soy dust**

was another important treatment for Bill, considering that he grew, harvested and handled soybeans on his farm. During the harvest, these allergens caused sporadic flare-ups. We implemented occasional bacteria immune focus over the next winter.

- **Gluten and gliadin**

were also key food components that we had to address.

Magnesium supplementation helped his sleep issue and probiotic supplementation continued to repair his intestinal flora. He was also thrilled that his wheezing incidents continued to decline.

Bill could feel the improvements and was very disciplined about taking his various nutritional supplements, as well as immediately calling into the office to make an appointment when he didn't feel right. That way, we were able to quickly catch any viruses or bacteria that were trying to make a comeback in his system.

The second spring after becoming a patient, we had to reinforce some of Bill's airborne allergen treatments, like pollen and dust. There are many different varieties of these allergens, e.g., soy dust, hay dust, barn dust, field dust, house dust, basement dust, bedroom dust and dust mites. These allergens require different sets of enzymes to show up (meaning to be epigenetically expressed), to break them down and process them inside the body.

Enzymes are encoded by genes that reside in our DNA. Nutritionally speaking, we supported Bill's liver rehabilitation, as the liver is the main detoxifying organ. Pesticides came up once again, in other words, whatever chemicals Bill was handling on the farm, we had to desensitize him to those chemicals.

Believe me, modern farmers handle a *lot* of chemicals, which is rather disturbing, given that they are producing our food supply with the help of these chemicals. Does anyone else believe that there is a connection between constantly increasing cancer rates and excessive amounts of chemicals used in agriculture?

Some seemingly trivial items also had to be treated in Bill's case:

- **diesel fumes,**
- **pork** and
- **bananas.**

During harvest time, Bill had one more asthma attack after harvesting and handling soybeans. I had previously treated him for soy dust, bacteria, and a virus, but I believe that those three groups converging at the same time triggered the event. Bill was using his rescue inhaler only very occasionally, such as in this episode, when an infection combined with dust simply overwhelmed his system.

During the second winter under my care, we were still treating spontaneous viral or bacterial assaults, but it was much easier for Bill's immune system to fight off these routine occurrences with some energetic immune support in the form of a SHOW treatment and natural medicine, including the use of Echinacea and cod liver oil.

Bill is now completely asthma-free, resulting in no more wheezing. It took almost two years and close to 50 treatments, because we had to treat the whole body, not just manage his asthma. Years of antibiotic treatments and inhaler use had left him extremely vulnerable. His innate intelligence is once again in charge and he doesn't get anywhere close to using up his $10,000 health insurance deductible. It now acts according to its intended purpose – as catastrophic coverage.

"For all the happiness mankind can gain; it's not in pleasure, but in rest from pain."

- John Dryden

Chapter 8 – Arthritis

Life goes on, and there is more to good health than "just" asthma and infections. Now we work on other aspects of Bill's life, such as epigenetically upregulating uric acid elimination to reduce inflammation caused by gout in his joints and thereby reducing his arthritis as he grows older.

---

*Gout - an extremely painful form of inflammatory arthritis caused by an accumulation of **uric acid crystals** in the joints. These crystals can also deposit in other tissues throughout the body, such as the kidney, which can lead to kidney stones. Gout is more common in men over the age of 45, but it can occur in anyone at any age. Factors range from a family history of gout to having other health issues, such as high blood pressure, diabetes, and heart or kidney disease.*

Over the years, I have learned that much of arthritis is caused by chronic gout. I also believe that we can now epigenetically upregulate the body's capacity to more effectively eliminate uric acid daily, by delivering resonating frequencies to the responsible genes. This was an important task to accomplish with Bill. He continues to enjoy the physical work on the farm and is doing very well at 58, living drug-free!

Commonly the Biofeedback treatments, which up-regulate uric acid elimination, consist of the frequencies of the enzyme **xanthine oxidase** with the frequencies of **DNA** and **hypothalamus** in combination.

The genes SLC2A9 and ABCG2, seem to have the greatest influence on urate levels. We now combine them with xanthine oxidase in gout treatments.

Hypoxanthine-guanine phosphoribosyl transferase (HGPRT) is an enzyme involved in the salvage of purine nucleotides. Reductions in HGPRT activity do cause hyperuricemia and gout due to the reduced salvage of hypoxanthine and guanine leading to increased uric acid production.

Increased levels of **PRPP,((5'-phosphoribosyl-1'-pyrophosphate, PRPP)** in turn, drive enhanced *de novo* synthesis of purine nucleotides in excess of the needs of the body. Thus, the excess purine nucleotides are catabolized resulting in elevated production of uric acid and consequent hyperuricemia and gout.

We do have the frequencies of these genes in the SHOW Method as well as the IMAET software and employ them as a biofeedback in balancing these functions for a harmonious uric acid metabolism.

Symptomatically, 'Tart Cherry Juice' can help clear out more uric acid. Kidney support with the Standard Process supplement 'Renafood' (App4) can also be helpful by supporting rehabilitation of the kidneys, elevating them to better function.

Uric acid is the end product of an exogenous pool of purines and endogenous purine metabolism. Animal proteins contribute significantly to this exogenous purine pool. The endogenous production of uric acid is mainly from the liver, intestines and other tissues like muscles, kidneys and the vascular endothelium.

It's a little like the cholesterol story, you get some from your diet, but your liver produces endogenous cholesterol/uric acid. Why, because they are essential to life. These compounds are NOT bad, they are only bad in excess. Very bad. To keep them in balance we need a balanced diet and, very importantly, we need to get the genes, which encode the responsible enzymes, working properly and efficiently. And the good news is:

WE CAN!

Xanthine Dehydrogenase / Xanthine Oxidase

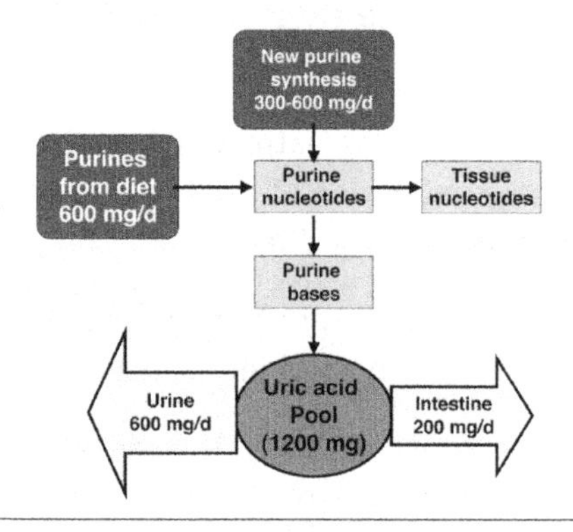

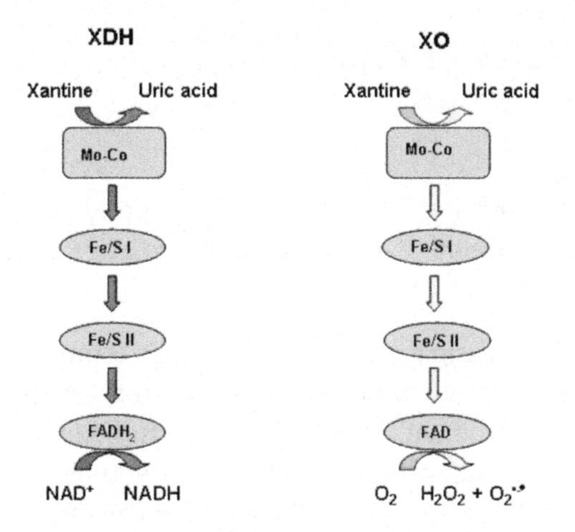

Xanthine Dehydrogenase / Xanthine Oxidase

Please note: The difference between urea and uric acid is:

1) Urea is a byproduct of protein metabolism, is liquid and contains ammonia. Too much ammonia is toxic to the body. Requires lots of water to flush out.

2) Uric Acid is a crystal, which is a byproduct of purine metabolism. Excess U.A. causes gout and kidney stones. Acidic pH and dehydration may increase U.A. (gout/arthritis) issues.

"The 3 Cs of life: choices, chances and changes. You must make a choice to take a chance or your life will never change." - *Unknown*

Chapter 9 – A Case of Teenage Acne

Sam, a 17-year-old high school senior, recently had a serious case of acne. He's slender, about 5'10", plays multiple sports, and is a moderate stud.

His face had the classic teenage acne look: his temples and sideburn area, the bridge of his nose, his forehead, and the area around his chin were all broken out in acne, some with visible whiteheads. You had to feel bad for the kid. He's kind, handsome, athletic, and smart… you almost want to kiss him on the forehead, but actually, probably not, given all the acne.

Unfortunately, many teenagers and young adults suffer from this condition, and treatment can come in many different forms.

What's *causing it*, however, is a state of toxicity. This toxicity originates from the output of androgens, a type of sex hormone. Hormones can become toxic when they accumulate, especially testosterone (and estrogen in women). Thyroid hormone is just as toxic, but it causes a different set of symptoms.

The organ in charge of detoxifying the body by eliminating excess hormones is the liver. Therefore, acne is often an indication of an overwhelmed or underperforming liver. The kidneys may also be involved, meaning that they're not clearing toxins out of the blood efficiently enough.

Another toxic state can occur due to allergies or chronic infections. Sam does have chronic sinus issues from airborne allergies, which may have contributed to his issue. These hidden conditions all produce a high toxic burden, and the liver simply can't process all of it. As a result, the toxins remain in the blood, and the body has no choice but to excrete them through the skin. That is the **etiology** of acne, and when those toxins come out through the skin, it isn't always pretty!

Etiology- the cause or set of causes, or manner of causation of a disease or condition.

To permanently get rid of acne, one must reduce the toxic burden on the liver and kidneys and increase their physiological function. We do this by stimulating and improving Bile Flow through the gallbladder. This allows the person to excrete toxins and be much healthier than when we started, rather than increasing the toxicity burden and negatively impacting health through the pharmaceutical management of symptoms.

In terms of Sam's treatment approach, we started out treating:

- **Eggs**
- **Chicken**
- **Sugar**
- **Dairy**
- **Pollen allergies**

We then focused his newly empowered immune system on eliminating an array of chronic viruses, such as the

- **common cold, flu, and viruses** related to vaccinations he had received.

We continued to improve his metabolism (which naturally improves the immune system) with allergy treatments of:

- **Vitamin C**
- **Berries**
- **Yeast**
- **Candida**
- **Fish and Vitamin A**

as well as various

- **chronic bacteria**.
- **parasites**
- even **iron** and **meat** had to be treated as allergies.
- **Tree nuts**

The acne didn't budge in the first two months of weekly SHOW treatments. However, in the third month, we saw some improvement in the severity of the skin breakouts. Throughout this epigenetic harmonization process, we nutritionally supported kidney and liver detoxification, bile flow Arginex and Betafood from Standard Process (App 5). We also supported the digestive system as a whole with a Probiotic.

---

*Bile flow - Bile is secreted by the liver into small ducts that join to form the **common hepatic duct**. Between meals, secreted bile is stored in the gallbladder. During a meal, the bile is secreted into the **duodenum** to rid the body of waste stored in the bile, as well as aid in the **absorption of dietary fats and oils**.*

(App 7))

We continued the treatment regimen by improving his

- **gluten and wheat digestion**, followed by treatments for
- **peanuts and nightshades**.

This was achieved through the SHOW Method procedures (App 1). Sam is a great sport, and he stuck with it from start to finish. Nutritional support was fine tuned for the kidneys and spleen during this segment of the treatment protocol.

It took six months and over a dozen holistic SHOW Method treatments, but once we started getting past the

- **hay fever** treatment and
- **drywall** allergy treatment,

all of Sam's symptoms began to improve.

I only see Sam occasionally now, namely when his immune system needs a focus or a boost, and when his back hurts after an athletic mishap or strain. He's going off to college soon, and his face is handsome, clean and healthy, which perfectly matches his personality. He's ready to face the world, including the bright lights of Hollywood, with an abundance of self-confidence radiating from his face!

In the process of harmonizing Sam's metabolism, we eliminated all his allergies, so his sinuses no longer bother him. His organs and his immune system are in excellent working order, and his body is back to detoxifying efficiently. He is prepared to mingle with the over-vaccinated and frequently sick college kid population and stand his ground, **drug-free.**

"It is so silly of people to fancy that old age means crookedness and witheredness and feebleness and sticks and spectacles and rheumatism and forgetfulness! It is so silly! Old age has nothing whatever to do with all that. The right old age means strength and beauty and mirth and courage and clear eyes and strong, painless limbs." - *George MacDonald*

Chapter 10 - Fibromyalgia

Helen is a 66-year-old divorced mother and grandmother. She has been dealing with fatigue and hypothyroidism all her adult life. The joints in her hands hurt and her feet ache, along with tingling and swelling. The joints in her hands had begun to get disfigured, and her right side hurt from her head down to her toes. She had been diagnosed with fibromyalgia, Sjogren's syndrome, Raynaud's and leukopenia (low white blood cell count). She never felt well, and her speech was extremely slow. She was on Lyrica for muscle and nerve pain, Amitriptyline for sleeping, and Allegra for her allergies, and Levothyroxine for her thyroid. She needed all those medications daily, and she rarely had what most of us think of as a "good" day.

Fibromyalgia is a rheumatic condition characterized by muscle pain in the joints throughout the body. In some cases, symptoms appear after a traumatic event, but most of the time, the symptoms gradually appear over time. Intermittent aches and pains become constant, the person begins to suffer from chronic fatigue, and is often unable to sleep, which can then lead to memory problems and depression. Anyone in constant pain is bound to have plenty of other problems associated with their symptoms.

Modern medicine cannot heal fibromyalgia; it can only try to alleviate the symptoms. Exercise is recommended, although how people are supposed to exercise when every inch of their body hurts has yet to be explained. Relaxation and stress management is also highly recommended. Again, this is very difficult to do, even with the best intentions in the world, when every joint you have is aching. For sufferers of fibromyalgia, it can seem like being stuck in a deep pit without a ladder to get out.

What complicated matters was that fibromyalgia was just one of the diseases Helen had been diagnosed with. Another one, leukopenia, is a reduction in white blood cells in the body, which means that it was very hard for Helen to fight off an infection without antibiotics. Sjogren's syndrome usually accompanies problems with the immune system, and the primary symptoms are a dry mouth and an inability to produce tears. Helen literally couldn't even cry about what was happening inside her body.

Upon entering the practice, Helen's health goal was to just feel a little better and have a bit more energy. She wasn't aiming for the moon; she just wanted to have a slightly better quality of life and perhaps a little more energy to do some of the things we all take forgranted.

So, we got to work immediately. After Helen's first treatment, where we treated her for reactions against:

- **egg white, egg yolk, chicken** and **feathers,**

she had a profound deep release experience. The muscles in her face and body released and brought Helen immediate and noticeable relief. On subsequent visits, we continued to treat Helen for more food allergies:

- **Treatment #2 - Calcium and milk**
- **#3 - Vitamin C**
- **#4 - Vitamin B complex**
- **#5 – Sugars**
- **#6 - Grains and gluten**
- **#7 - Iron and meat**

We also desensitized airborne allergies:

- **Tree pollen**
- **Springtime pollen**
- **Hay fever and weeds**
- **Chronic viral and parasitic infections**
- **Yeasts and molds**

While going through this treatment regimen of epigenetic modulation of Helen's metabolism over the next few months, we harmonized (treated):

- **Vitamin A**
- **Hepatitis E virus and EBV (Epstein Barr virus)**

- **Salt**
- **Household chemicals**
- **Peanuts and beans**
- **Minerals**
- **Animal fats**

The treatment protocol included probiotics as a supplement, taken on an empty stomach, to heal the gut. Probiotics are beneficial bacteria in the gut and are part of a healthy microbiome.

Gut – A synonym for Gastrointestinal tract.

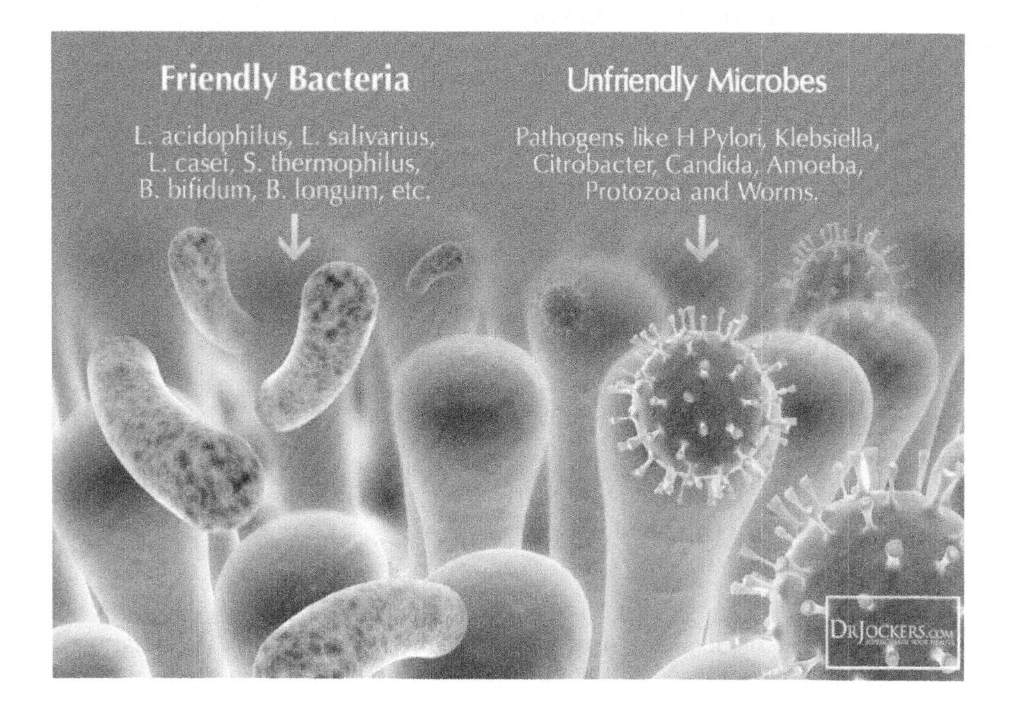

Why take probiotics on an empty stomach?
They are destined for the small intestine and must pass through the stomach to get there. Stomach acid will kill the fragile beneficial bacteria. The less food in the stomach, the less acid present, and the higher the survival rate for the actual probiotic.

*A **biome** is a community of plants and animals living together in a certain kind of climate. The human **microbiome** is the genetic material of all the microbes - bacteria, fungi, protozoa and viruses - that live on and inside the **human** body. The number of genes in all the microbes in one person's **microbiome** is 200 times the number of genes in the **human** genome. The **microbiome** may weigh as much as five pounds.*

Her allergies were clearly dissipating, and the first medication to go was Allegra. We continued treating her for:

- **tree nuts** and
- **nightshades**,

and then addressed some of her environmental sensitivities like

- **carpets and carpet glue**,

things that most people never even think about, because they are not aware of all their sensitivities.

Helen's blood work improved, and the frightening diagnosis of leukopenia disappeared; Helen would now be able to fight infections on her own, with less need for constant antibiotics. What a relief! Now that her body was stronger, we could start addressing some emotional issues and chronic infections, since her immune system had grown stronger.

Lyrica and Amitriptyline are habit-forming drugs, so it took some effort to wean her off of them. But she did it, under careful supervision, consisting of diligent MRT for focused nutritional support. Today, only one year after starting on this path, Helen is basically a different person. She feels much better, experiences far less pain, and is therefore on a lot less medication, which means she not only saves money, but also doesn't have to deal with the side effects from all those medications. Her speech is more normal, and her demeanor is much more present and engaged. She is still taking her thyroid medication.

Helen's journey is continuing, but from here on, it will be with far less medication and much more vitality!

"I took a deep breath and listened to the old brag of my heart; I am, I am, I am." -
Sylvia Plath, The Bell Jar

Chapter 11 - Low Back Pain – severe episodes

When Debbie, a mother of two and a teacher in her 30s, entered our clinic for the first time, she was hanging onto her husband's side, taking baby steps and wailing in agony. I was amazed she hadn't arrived on a stretcher. Her lower back was "completely giving out." Apparently, this had been happening many times before with visits to Urgent Care and the ER, sometimes even with ambulance pickups.

She came to my office because her husband had heard from one of his clients about our clinic with its holistic approach. They wanted to try chiropractic, which was completely different than their usual unsuccessful approach of painkillers, narcotics and muscle relaxers.

It was immediately clear to me that this was not a case of "my back went out"—meaning some vertebrae had slipped or a vertebral disc was pinching a nerve. It's true that these progressive degenerative disease diagnoses will eventually occur, given enough time and medical treatment. However, a lot less of this goes on than you'd think, and you may be surprised as to the actual cause of low back pain (LBP). It was obvious to me right away, that Debbie's predicament was a severe bout of inflammation originating from allergies and latent infections. In fact, her sinuses were chronically stuffy, and she reported recurrent sinusitis. When it comes to the spine and lower back, that same inflammation affects the ligaments around the vertebrae of the lumbar spine and the deep back muscles, which go into spasm. All this causes severe pain and leads to ligament sprain injury and muscle strain injury. So, what's the obvious answer to appease the acute pain episode, as well as the more long-term prospects of recurrence and arthritic degeneration? Stop the inflammation immediately!

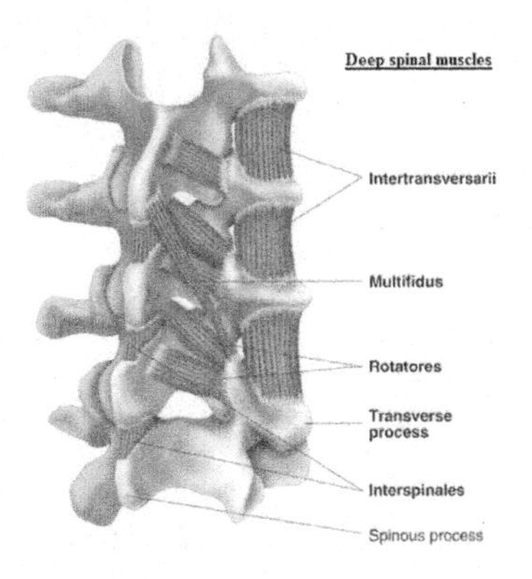

Then one can focus on repairing the muscular injury. Instead of using steroids, narcotic painkillers and muscle relaxers, we got to work on the underlying issues right away. "You have allergies," I said. "I know," Debbie replied, "but my back is killing me."

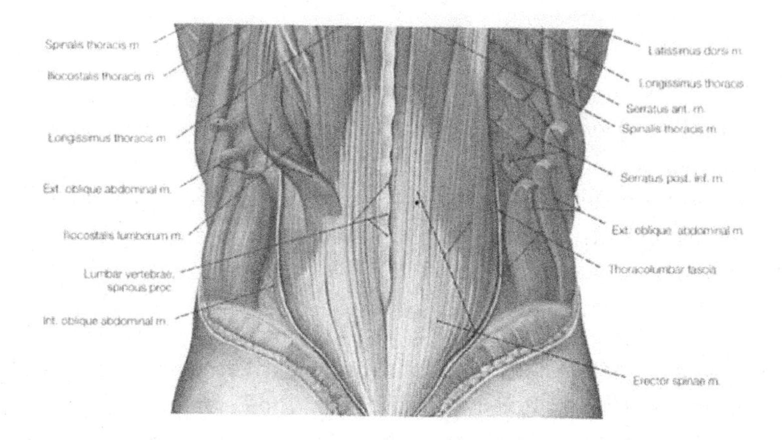

Top layer of lumbar muscles and fascia.

After muscle testing, we started treating her Grains and Gluten allergy with the SHOW Method protocol. This allowed her Vitamin B allergies to surface. There are a couple of dozen B vitamins in the Vitamin B Complex. It always amazes me how common Vitamin B allergies really are. Everybody who has health issues of any sort seems to have some Vitamin B allergies. Vitamin B12, B9 (Folic Acid) and B6 are involved in the methylation cycle and are therefore particularly important.

Methylation Cycle - is a biochemical pathway that manages or contributes to a wide range of crucial bodily functions, including:

- *Genetic expression and repair of the DNA*
- *Inflammation response*
- *Detoxification of hormones, chemicals, and heavy metals*
- *Metabolism of a most important anti-oxidant called glutathione*
- *Neurotransmitter formation and breakdown.*
- *Mood balancing*
- *Cellular energy production and mitochondrial health*
- *Immune response and function*

Methylation Cycle

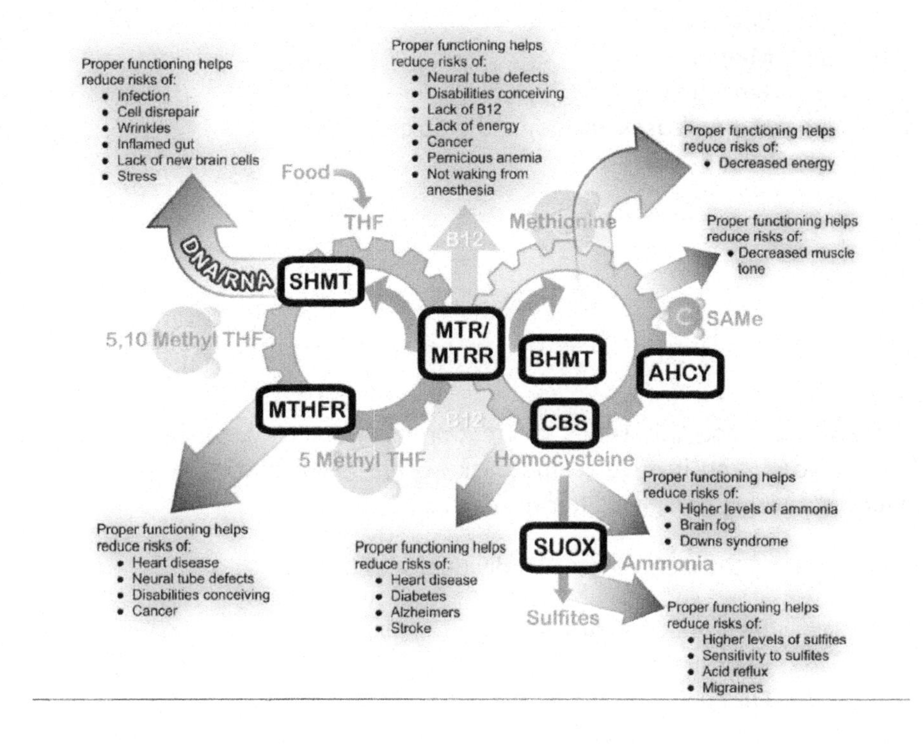

Most 'famous' of late is the MTHFR (methylenetetrahydrofolate reductase) SNP or mutation within the methylation cycle. The MTHFR gene activates Folate by methylating it (adding a methyl group CH3). It is reported that over 90% of children with Autism have this mutation.

However, initially with Debbie, we harmonized the entire Vitamin B Complex, not just Folate. After the Vitamin B Complex, we treated

- **grains & gluten**

Then we focused on the following allergens, harmonized their metabolism per SHOW Method (in NAET this is called 'clearing' the allergen) and addressed chronic infections:

- **Animal dander**
- **Wheat & Gliadin**
- **Grain alcohol**
- **Mold & fungus**
- **Corn**

- **CMV (cytomegalovirus) & Shingles virus**
- **Dust**
- **Bacteria**
- **Magnesium**
- **Tree nuts**
- More **viruses**, including the **Coxsackie virus**

There is growing evidence that latent ***CMV*** *infections are part of the etiology of glioblastoma, a serious brain cancer.*

Somewhere along this series of treatments, Debbie's Low Back Pain was completely gone, and it never came back in this severe way. Yet, her sinuses continued bothering her, giving her headaches.

We continued the treatments in individual sessions:

- **Tree pollen & flowers**
- **Perfumes**
- **Fungus**

As it turns out, the sinuses were much more challenging than the lower back. We had to clear (harmonize) B vitamins emotionally. Allergies happen in roughly three different ways:

1) Leaky gut from poor gut health.

2) SNPs and mutations in the genome.

3) Emotional blockages from emotional traumas. Emotional blockages are addressed with a special procedure, slightly different from the standard food allergy EHT (Epigenetic harmonization treatment) of the SHOW Method.

The inflammation in Debbie's sinuses turned yet again into a bacterial infection. Debbie's infections were relentless, one after another. I don't know how she survived all these years like this, with multiple antibiotic treatments per year. However, this time she handled the infection not with antibiotics, but by unleashing her own immune system with SHOW Method biofeedback treatments. In her perception, the back pain and her allergies had no connection. But they are very much connected. The inflammation generated by the allergies causes the sinusitis as well as the low back pain. We had to visit and revisit a few more allergies:

- **Aftershave**
- **Mosquitoes**
- **HPV** (human papilloma virus)
- **Vegetable fats**
- **Molds** and more fungi

Ever so slowly, the airborne allergies subsided. As Debbie's sinuses became normal, her headaches resolved. It took only 6 months and about 10 treatments to permanently rid Debbie of her bouts of LBP, although it took almost 2 years to get rid of her allergies driving the recurrent sinusitis and latent infections.

While we addressed her airborne allergies, Debbie went through a period of severe itching. Zyrtec helped the itching, so I knew her symptoms were allergy related with a histamine response. As we moved through the second year of harmonizing Debbie's genetic expression and balancing her cellular energy flow, we went through the following additional treatments:

- **Clorox & cleaning chemicals & bleach**
- **Preservatives, MSG & nitrates**
- **Ants**
- **Mast cells**
- **Agent orange & weed killer**
- **Detergents**
- **Water chemicals**
- **Molds** such as trichophyton met., rhizome nigra, and dermatophyton cong.

Debbie had one more sinus flare-up in the spring of the third year of becoming a patient at our clinic. After more than 20 energy harmonizing treatments (NAET and SHOW), she still reacted to certain food and environmental allergens and was treated for the following items:

- **Dust**
- **Flowers, weeds & tree pollen**
- **Phenolics**
- **Vitamin C**
- **Vitamin A**
- **Shellfish**

Through this last treatment protocol, uric acid showed up as a co-morbidity factor. We treated it by upregulating the enzyme Xanthine Oxidase in combination with the airborne items.

You might not think that Debbie is a good example for how to resolve low back pain, as her chronic sinusitis, headaches, itching and many infections dominated her day-to-day symptoms. However, it's important to recognize that after resolving her most fundamental allergies, the back pain was history. It may seem like a long time, over 2 years and more than 25 energy treatments. However, her issues are resolved, including an HPV issue (which causes female cancers). Plus, her body is functioning as it should. She has a much better quality of life and a much better prognosis for quality longevity. What would have been the alternative? More antibiotics, more antihistamines and other meds. And yes, after 3 years, she still would be dealing with bouts of excruciating low back pain, with a prognosis of low back surgery or at the least, degenerative arthritis. So, no, it's not always entirely easy to choose this road of energy balancing and precision stress reduction at the epigenetic level, but it sure is worth it.

Debbie kept telling me it was worth it. That it changed her life. And as a clinician, I was gratified to get to the root of her problem (her allergies) instead of just treating her symptoms the low back pain. Debbie was so grateful for the results; she brought her children in to be treated for their allergies. Because they were so young, their allergies cleared much more rapidly. However, if Debbie had come for treatment before she had children, the children would have had even fewer allergic and inflammatory issues because many benefits of energy balancing SHOW treatments are heritable.

Debbie got more than she bargained for. She came in with severe, acute Low Back Pain. She ended up with having multiple other serious health issues resolved. Isn't that what doctors are supposed to be doing, connecting the dots for people, rather than getting them hooked on addictive pain killers! **Chiropractic** treatments work well for the acute treatment of low back pain. Her husband had the instinct of realizing that there was more to these recurring episodes and brought her to a Holistic chiropractor, who also practices the SHOW Method and ASR Biofeedback.(App 16)

***Heritable** – able to be inherited.*
A characteristic transmissible from parent to offspring.

"An ounce of prevention is worth a pound of cure." *- Benjamin Franklin*

Chapter 12 - HPV (Human Papilloma Virus)

One of the most amazing benefits of the SHOW Method and the clinical use of the IMAET System is their capacity to not only recognize infections of all kinds but do something about them! What does "do something about them" mean? Basically, it means that we're able to communicate with the immune system at the epigenetic level and modulate its function. Once we do that, we can focus it on a specific pathogen and trigger the cascade of biochemical events necessary to launch an effective immune response.

Meet Alexa, a lean, 50-year-old woman with a history of anorexia, a former child fashion model with a promiscuous past, and years of misguided medical care. She initially came to see me regarding her ongoing and worsening struggle with anorexia, anxiety and depression. When I first met her, she was little more than skin and bones. She was a mess and knew that something had to change. Her MD had tried to counter her anorexia issues with Synthroid (thyroid hormone) therapy to forcefully speed up her metabolism. However, her thyroid function was *completely normal.* She was on five different psychotropic meds, including anti-depressants, anti-anxiety and anti-seizure drugs. She was a mess... and she felt like it. Sadly, it was something I'd seen many times before – a pharmaceutical-dependent lifestyle taking a brutal toll on a person's body. She was intelligent, articulate, well educated, aware of good nutrition, and even ate healthy food (when she actually ate). I knew that there was hope for her, and I was determined to find a way to help.

Once I understood her background and medical history, we got to work. We started checking her for some basic food allergies and the associated metabolic errors with the SHOW Method principles. We had to balance many basic nutrients, which is necessary in most patients. We then began healing her gut and confidently assured her that she wouldn't gain weight if she stopped taking that unnecessary thyroid medication. One prescription down, 12 to go....

Throughout this process, I repeatedly spotted HPV in her computer scans with the IMAET System. Finally, I told Alexa about the HPV and strongly suggested that we "do something about it"; specifically, I wanted to focus her immune system on eliminating this infection. She proceeded to tell me that her

PAP smears had been positive for the past 25 years and that her GYNs were keeping a close watch on the problem.

IMAET System scan result.

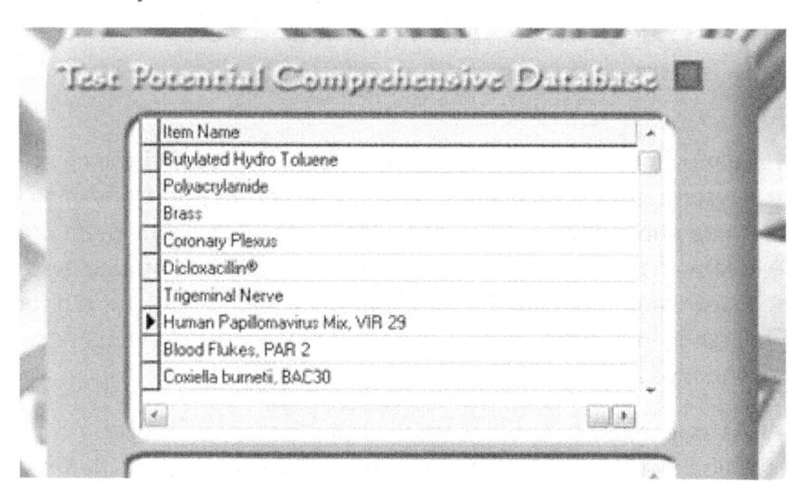

Human Papillomavirus (HPV) infection causes nearly all cervical ***cancers****. ... Smoking may increase the risk of cervical* ***cancer*** *for women who have* ***HPV****.* (cancer.net)

The medical model suggests, every woman with chronic **HPV** will be watched for dysplasia of the cervix. Cryotherapy and laser therapy burn off the affected tissues, and *Bingo*, problem solved. Really?! Something about that doesn't sound quite right. So, in between all the metabolic modulations of allergens, we also focused Alexa's immune system on neutralizing the HPV. I implemented a treatment protocol and every time the beast (HPV) reared its ugly head, we refocused her immune system on the menace. The timeline for this custom protocol went something like this:

Initial treatment – repeat one month later – repeat two months after that – and then repeat three months after that. Six months after the last treatment, HPV attempted another comeback. However, lo and behold, Alexa had her first negative Pap smear in 25 years. One year after that, we did a final follow- up. That was the last HPV treatment and her biannual PAP smears have been negative ever since. In other words, a chronic infection of 25 years or more cannot be eliminated overnight. Granted, if this had been Alexa's only health issue, we could have done it much faster, but we were working on multiple fronts in a truly holistic fashion to save this woman from cancer and whatever genetic expression her pharmaceutical lifestyle had in store for her.

It is accepted medical knowledge that chronic HPV infections can cause cervical cancer, and in my opinion, the uterine, ovarian and breast cancers that are so prevalent today are also part of those etiologies. This is especially true

BRCA 1 - a human tumor suppressor gene, a 'caretaker gene,' found in all humans; its protein, also called by the synonym breast cancer type 1 susceptibility protein, is responsible for repairing DNA.

when the infection works in combination with certain oncogenes, such as the BRCA 1 and BRCA 2 genes.

BRCA2 - a gene on chromosome 13 that normally helps to suppress cell growth. A person who inherits certain mutations (changes) in a BRCA2 gene has a higher risk of getting breast, ovarian, prostate, and other types of cancer. (National Cancer Institute)

Fortunately, we can work effectively against the epigenetic expression of those genes, whether you're aware of their variances and associated risks or not. The SHOW Method is able to "dig up" these dispositions because it looks for them.

The scientific research community is making incredible discoveries in epigenetics every day. Alexa was almost certainly on a path to developing cervical cancer, and with a more susceptible genome, she would have likely already been a victim. In this particular department, however, she was in "good health". We helped Alexa avoid cancer, a fact that gives me a great deal of satisfaction.

Alexa is much healthier now and has gotten off most of her meds. She continues to battle with anxiety, which has emotional cross-connections and has proven more difficult to resolve than all her other issues. Some integrative modalities, such as meditation and psychotherapy may help her to further deal with the chronic anxiety problem. (App 8)

The lure of pharmaceutical medication as a quick solution to a difficult problem is ever present and only a doctor's visit away. I hope that Alexa has found confidence in her own body's healing powers. And I hope she cherishes her real vitality enough to maintain it naturally as she moves on with her life.

"Tis better to understand than to be understood." - *Saint Francis of Assisi*

Chapter 13 - Lyme Disease

Today people are downright scared of Lyme (disease). The perception is that our immune systems are helpless and incapable to confront Lyme. Politicians are even using the epidemic and the people's fear of Lyme to score points with the public. But not so fast. I have developed a code language, the SHOW Method, to actually communicate with the Immune System in a very precise manner, through bioenergetic frequencies.

Jenn was referred by her sister, a practicing Reiki Master and Young Living oils enthusiast. However, her situation, as she explained, needed some professional attention.

Jenn presented with back pain, which was unusual for her. She had contracted Lyme disease some weeks before and had the positive ELISA test to prove it. Many people have Lyme disease and the laboratory diagnostic result is negative, especially in the chronic cases. However, Jenn had a positive test and was still in the acute phase. She had the Borrelia antibody. She also mentioned a shingles outbreak that had occurred a year earlier, which is often considered a sign of a weak immune system. So, we got to work immediately.

Borrelia burgdorferi is a spirochete, an order of slender spirally undulating bacteria causing Lyme disease. There are many different Spirochetes. They also cause syphilis and dental plaque.

In the first few treatments, we focused the immune system on the

- **Borrelia burgdorferi spirochete** (3 treatment sessions)

and used immune-supporting herbs like Cat's Claw, Echinacea and shiitake mushrooms.

Borrelia burgdorferi dark field illumination.

American Society of Microbiology.

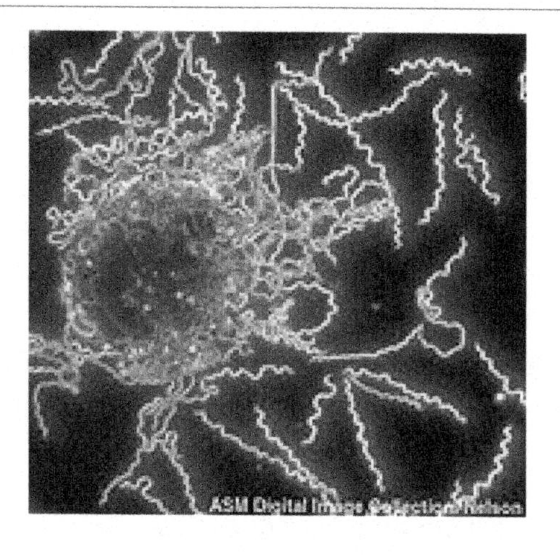

We continued Jenn's treatment regimen with various metabolic energy treatments or clearances (SHOW Method) of the following basic nutrients:

- **B Vitamins**
- **Grains** and **gluten**

The continuous treatments over the next few weeks followed the immune trail as it presented at each visit by IMAET scanning or MRT, revealing some common viruses, and other varieties of bacteria, including some exotic ones:

- ***Bartonella***

Initially, Jenn was being treated twice a week, and we made quick progress. Her back pain subsided after a few weeks and we followed up with:

- **Hay fever** desensitization

it happened to be hay fever season.

- **Wheat** and some of its components (gliadin, lectin, phenol)

Whether ***Borrelia burgdorferi*** showed up in the computer scan or not, we added that frequency to the feedback or treatment.

During the first month of treatments, Jenn didn't feel much better, complaining of insomnia, muscle pain and joint pain, which were all worse at night. A few key supplements, including magnesium citrate, eased the symptoms during these episodes.

We diligently worked on Jenn's allergies and immune issues as they presented and continued to nutritionally build up her immune system with natural medicines, such as Immuplex from Standard Process (App 5) and cod liver oil. Nutritional Thyroid support was indicated about two weeks into the process. By the second month, she was down to one treatment every two weeks. We covered these allergens with SHOW Method biofeedback treatments:

- **Parasites**
- **Molds**
- **Sugars**
- **Eggs**
- **Fats**

Jenn's MD was pressuring her to take antibiotics, and I even recommended that she do one course of antibiotics, just to shorten the ordeal. However, Jenn never filled the prescription.

The treatment protocol continued with:

- **Candida** and **yeast**.

She reported visual disturbances after this treatment, from the fungal die-off, which is known as a **Herxheimer Reaction.**

Herxheimer Reaction - (i.e., herxing or die-off) is the release of endotoxins from the destroyed cell walls of bacteria or fungi, that causes an additional inflammatory response (i.e., debilitating physical and mental state) contingent on the number of endotoxins released, which is directly correlated to the number of bacteria or fungi killed.

Two weeks of probiotic therapy followed, along with cleaning up her system or body, eliminating a garden variety of co-infections:

- **Bacteria**
- **Viruses**
- **Parasites**
- **Molds**

Simultaneous infection by several pathogens is very common with Lyme disease. Truth be told, it's true for all weak immune systems. The secret is to identify these infections energetically and guide the immune system to focus on each one of those categories. In acute cases this means very early on, in chronic cases it means even if not detectable by laboratory testing. We even expanded to Jenn's chemical sensitivities, which she had to deal with all her life, and we were able to harmonize how her body dealt with environmental allergens.

By the third month of treatment, Jenn was doing much better. The acute back pain had disappeared, she was sleeping better, and her body aches were all but gone. Some brain fog and overall energy lags were the only complaints that remained.

Jenn was feeling very good, even better than her pre-Lyme self. However, she explained her opinion that the Lyme was in her backyard and that her animals had it too, which made her worry about reinfection.

After the four-month treatment protocol and about 15 SHOW biofeedback treatments, Jenn's immune system is significantly stronger. I would venture to say that she is not only Lyme-free, but also much more resistant to re-infection from any pathogen in the future, including Borrelia burgdorferi. During Jenn's treatment process, we literally exercised her immune system and with the SHOW treatments, guided her Immune System towards eliminating multiple infections. The adaptive Immune System earns and has a memory. Each encounter makes the Immune System stronger, if it gets a chance to fight it off on its own. Constantly doing Antibiotics deprives the Immune System from becoming mature and powerful.

During this treatment period, we also balanced and improved Jenn's metabolic function by increasing nutrient availability to the immune system. After all of that, she is now much more prepared for a future microbial assault of any kind. So even if the Lyme danger is close to her own house, she is in good shape to stand her ground.

The Immune System works many unpleasant details of life:

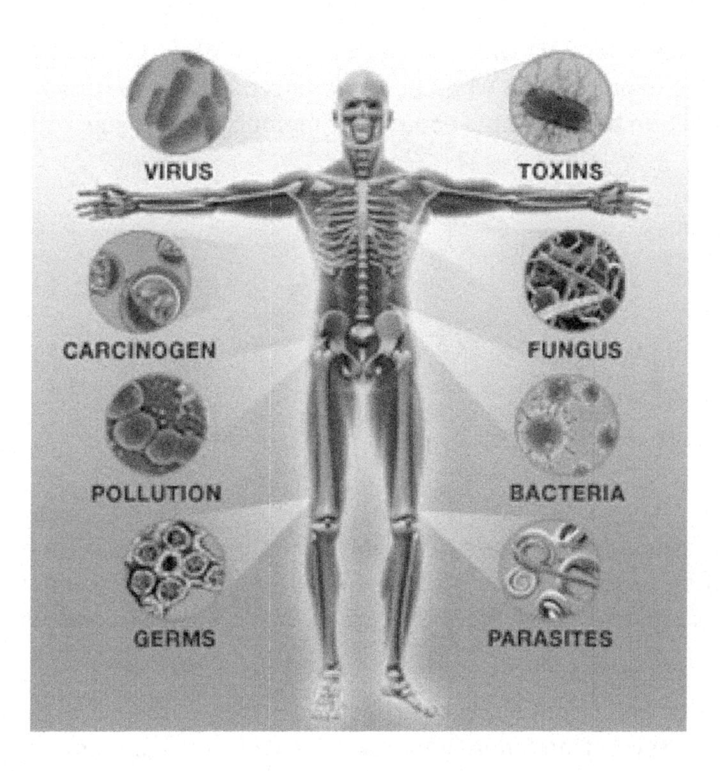

From a philosophical point of view, it certainly appears reasonable, maybe even smart, to invest into a healthy, powerful Immune System, which has helped us to survive for thousands of years. The notion to rely heavily on vaccination as a health strategy may be short-sighted and potentially dangerous. Certainly, health statistics seem to indicate a steady decline in fundamental health as vaccinations schedules increase.

"Laugh and the world laughs with you, snore and you sleep alone."

- Anthony Burgess

Chapter 14 – Sleep Apnea

Mike, a dairy farmer, was referred to my practice by one of his church members. His main concern when he came into the office was heartburn and GERD, in addition to complaints about poor memory and fatigue.

GERD – Gastro esophageal Reflux Disease
A chronic disease that occurs when stomach acid or bile flows into the food pipe and irritates the lining.

Mike presented with classic "leaky gut" symptoms, caused by intestinal candida. Impressively, we resolved that crucial issue on his very first visit. *How were we able to accomplish that in one week, while others struggle with candida for years?*

Well, first and foremost, Mike probably didn't have the worst case of candida ever; second, and more importantly, we involved his Immune System in the process, which was a crucial factor. We focused Mike's Immune System on ridding the intestine of the pesky fungus. Yes, believe it or not, the immune system basically controls everything in the body, even fungus elimination. We didn't have to use antifungals either, just a simple regimen of **probiotics** to re-inoculate the intestinal mucosa with beneficial bacteria. Once the candida fungus vacates the intestine, yes by force of the Immune System, it is essential that beneficial bacteria, like Lactobacillus and Boulardii take its place.

These beneficial bacteria facilitate the absorption of nutrients through the gut, whereas the fungus causes leaks in the intestinal wall lining. Such damage allows incompletely digested food components to escape into the bloodstream, causing allergic reactions and inflammation (hence the name "leaky gut"). It is a bit disheartening that the medical mainstream still insists on debunking this widely known and researched phenomenon.

***Probiotics** - live bacteria and yeasts that are good for your health, especially for your digestive system. They assist in the absorption of digested nutrients through the gut wall for transfer into the bloodstream and subsequent delivery to the cells.*

Mike's heartburn/GERD problems resolved rapidly. We proceeded to harmonize and clear these basic food components:

- **Vitamin B complex,**
- **grains and gluten**.

These are common allergens, yet extremely important for the function of digestion, absorption and energy.

On the next visit, we followed up with a

- **sugar** treatment.

After the sugar-harmonizing treatment, Mike's heartburn seemed to disappear.

At that point, he proceeded to tell me that his wife was very happy about the treatments he was receiving, because his **sleep apnea** had greatly improved. Sleep apnea? Hhmmm. He didn't tell me about sleep apnea because he never imagined that this humble chiropractor could remedy such an issue. This meant that his wife's sleep was far less interrupted. In addition, he was no longer kicking her in the middle of the night, which obviously improved <u>her</u> quality of sleep and soothed any frayed nerves and frustrations.

His wife was clearly thrilled and highly supportive of his treatments. In fact, she has since also become a patient, albeit for a different set of issues.

Mike had never told me about his sleep apnea, but we managed to fix it anyway! He's not obese; obesity exacerbates sleep apnea, and by harmonizing his metabolism with four treatments and healing his gut, his sleep apnea disappeared quickly. We're now working on further improving his energy levels, fighting his chronic fatigue and rehabilitating his thyroid function.

Good health is a complex, holistic and very individual affair. This is only one of countless examples of how a comprehensive and personal approach can do wonders for a patient's quality of life.

Since these initial "successes," Mike is a regular patient at our clinic, and if something new concerns *him, he comes here first. Recently, he experienced a moderate spike in his blood pressure. We* scanned his body with the IMAET System, and from the results performed energy-balancing procedures on just 2 groups of 'allergens'.

- **Fabrics (**different kind of common fabrics)
- **Vitamin A** (the Complex).

On his follow-up visit, his blood pressure was back to 'low normal.'

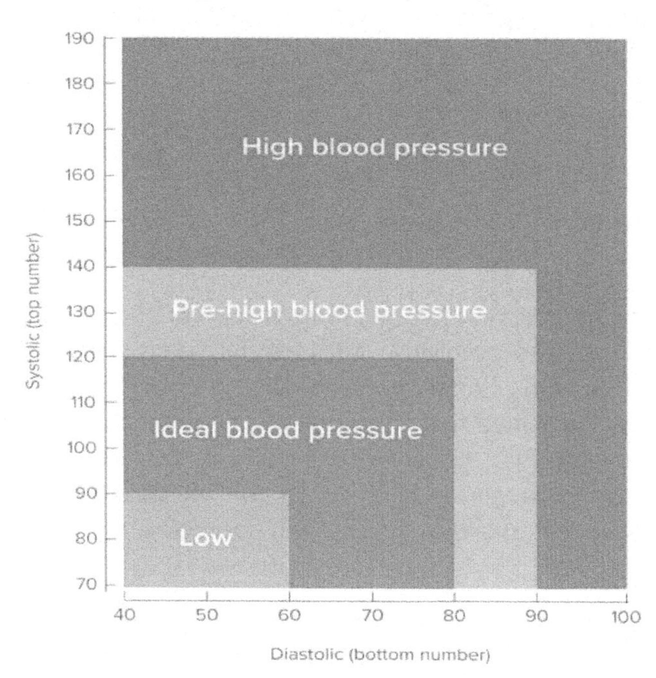

Blood Pressure can be a tough issue, can be complicated, and certainly is not always as quickly balanced as in this case. However, I want to point out, that if we consistently look for the causes of health issues (Blood pressure, Cholesterol, pain etc), early on, starting in childhood and try to resolve these issues, rather then medicate them right away, we will end up with a much healthier individual, healthier people and in my humble opinion, a healthier society.

Note: Since the first edition of this book, the AHA (American Heart Association) has lowered the acceptable BP limits to 130/80. I believe this is in the service of getting more people on medications rather than in the interest of public health. A Blood Pressure of 140/80 as a high limit is very reasonable in my opinion.

"It is easier to build strong children than to repair broken men."

- *Frederick Douglass, abolitionist and statesman*

Chapter 15 - Sensory Integration Disorder (SID)

Jordan came into my practice when he was only three, after developing a streptococcal pneumonia infection following a Prevnar 13 vaccination shot. He was prone to infections, both bacterial and viral, and often developed rashes and little bumps on his skin in conjunction with those infections.

In order to strengthen his young immune system, we identified his food allergies energetically through kinesiology, computer software (IMAET System) or testing vials, all representing associated innate frequencies of different vitamins, minerals, amino acids, phenols and fats (fatty acids). The following order of treatment emerged:

- **Eggs/chicken**
- **Grains**
- **Gluten/gliadin**
- **Nightshades**
- **Vitamin B complex**
- **Sugars**
- **Vitamin C**
- **Milk/lactose**

In conjunction with these metabolic treatments, we exercised Jordan's Immune System by communicating with it and focusing it on various chronic viruses and bacteria that his body harbored and allowing his Immune System to get the job done on its own, producing Immune memory cells in the process.

How does one communicate with the Immune System?

Through subtle energies, represented by electromagnetic frequencies. Technically the frequencies look like this:

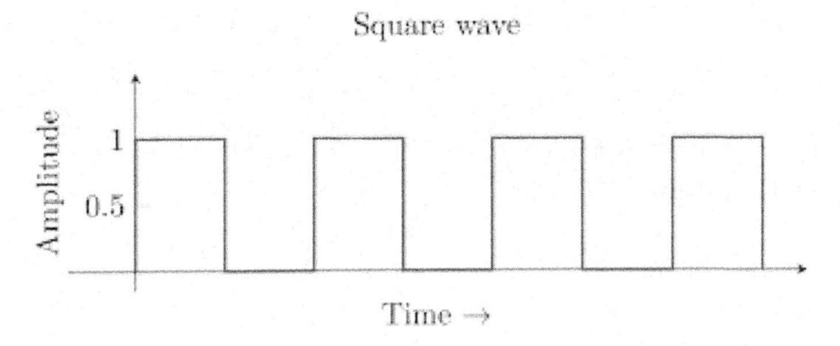

This represents the breakthrough in understanding the Energetic Paradigm presented in this book: the ability to communicate and interact with our DNA, epigenetically, through Subtle Energies represented by frequencies, which generate (non-ionizing) electromagnetic fields.

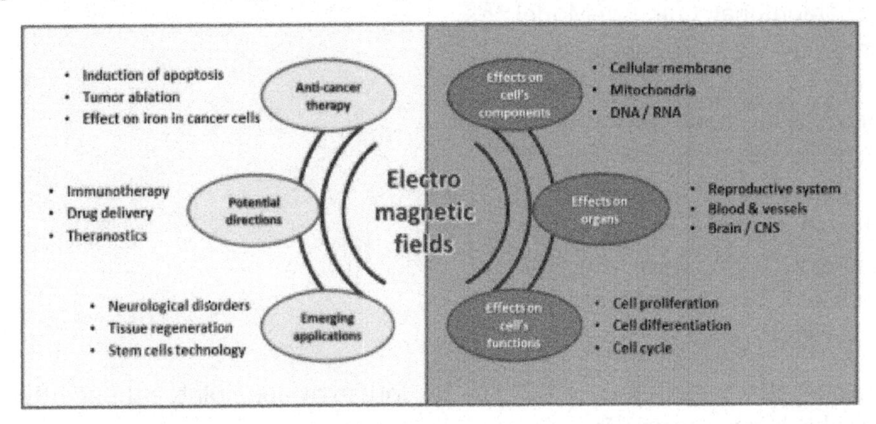

This can be achieved with energy imprinted vials (water) or with modern Quantum Biofeedback technology like the IMAET System.

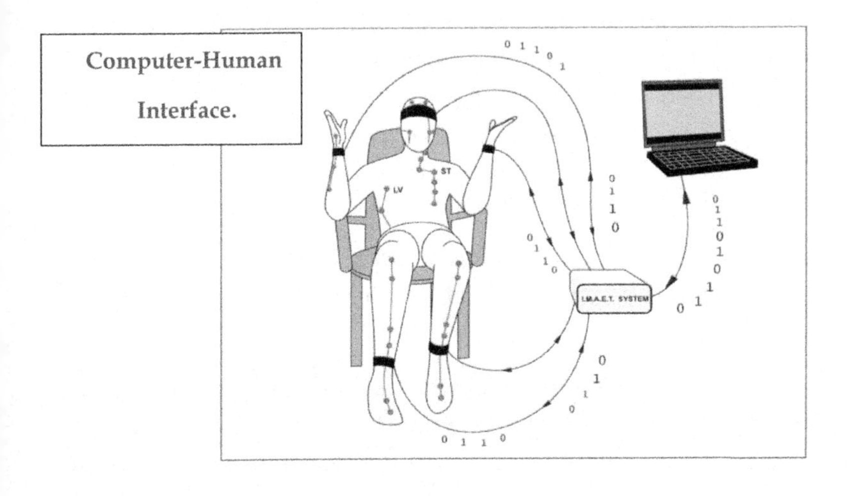

There are many different electromagnetic applications, from Pulsed Electromagnetic Field therapy (PEMF) to RIFE devices to Neurofeedback, The SHOW Method focuses on direct communication and modulation of epigenetic expression at the cellular level. This requires a particular precision to be able to resonate with specific genes, receptors and functional gene clusters. We're entering the field of functional genomics.

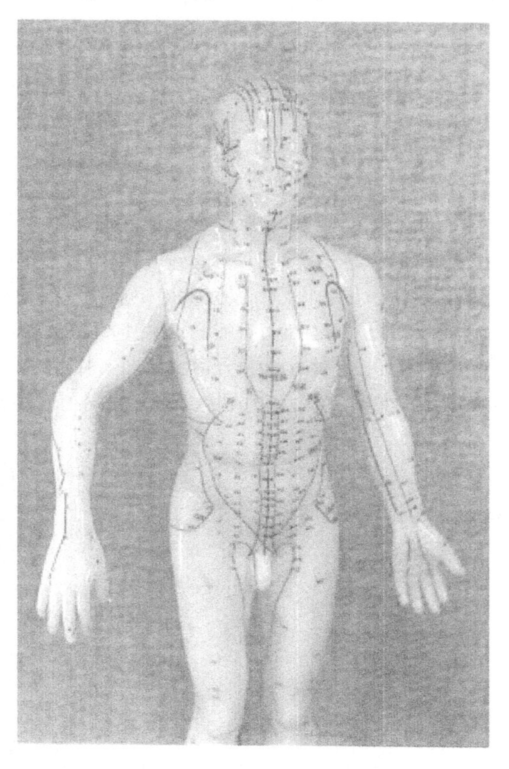

The Traditional Chinese Model of energy flow (Qi), represented by acupuncture is helpful in visualizing this information flow between all 100 trillion cells of the body. I look at the meridian system from TCM as the internet of the cells. Through these energy channels we can scan and modulate the energetic content of that Qi energy.

Parasites also became a serious issue for Jordan at one point, although this had probably been going on for some time. Pinworms was the most difficult one to eliminate. In fact, his brother and the rest of the family had to cleanse themselves of pinworms too.

As Jordan moved through his toddler years and experienced the horrendous vaccination schedule that comes with being that age and entering the school system, we responded to his metabolic struggles as quickly as they appeared. At the age of five, his pediatrician commented on his low platelet count. I treated him for yeast and intestinal candida, along with an antifungal herb (oregano oil) and probiotics, causing that issue to disappear almost immediately.

After yet another vaccination at age seven, his mother brought him in with a bit of concern, saying Jordan had just been diagnosed by his pediatrician with Sensory Integration Disorder (SID).

The presence of a sensory integration disorder is typically detected in young children. Most children develop sensory integration during ordinary childhood activities, such as play, which helps establish such things as the ability for motor planning and adapting to incoming sensations. When that process is disordered, a variety of problems in learning, development or behavior become apparent. Jordan's mom was puzzled by Jordan showing several odd behaviors, such as putting on girls' clothes and playing with dolls.

In order to figure out what the problem with Jordan's SID might be, we looked at his energetic status:

I could see certain hormonal imbalances in his IMAET computer scans. With this new information, we kept working on his metabolic imbalances, food allergies and immune issues, such as chronic infections. Over the course of three months, I treated him for energy imbalances to:

- **Shellfish** and **fish**
- **Progesterone**
- **Soy** and **Somatostatin**

Somatostatin- is a hormone produced by many tissues in the body, principally in the nervous and digestive systems. It regulates a wide variety of physiological functions and inhibits the secretion of other hormones, the activity of the gastrointestinal tract and the rapid reproduction of normal and tumor cells. Somatostatin may also act as a neurotransmitter in the nervous system.

Jordan also needed supplementation with Vitamin K for a few weeks. Furthermore, Jordan had an interesting hormonal imbalance that we quickly and successfully addressed with an Energy harmonizing treatment (SHOW).

I "followed the trail" of his body's metabolic imbalances, harmonized them by modulating epigenetic expression with very specific biofeedback treatments according to the SHOW Method, and supplemented appropriate nutritional factors. It was like a puzzle that we could never fully solve. One issue would always lead to another, but it did feel like we were making progress.

Jordan responded very well to the treatments, and the Sensory Integration Disorder dissipated over the following three months. Today, Jordan is 11 years old and a healthy, rambunctious, superhero-loving boy who adores everything typically considered masculine, such as trucks, guns, fatigues and sports.

Clearly, "listening to the body" and monitoring the details of metabolism is crucial in harmonizing a person. And when it comes to the constantly evolving metabolism and the immune systems of children, we can help guide those crucial systems in developing in a strong and healthy direction. It's possible to grow up and thrive without allergies, without serious immune weakness, and without a lifetime of drugs. A healthy and self-sufficient existence is not too much to ask. Last but not least, by harmonizing this boy's epigenetic function, he will someday pass on a stronger genome to his children and they will be able to develop a strong and healthy metabolism of their own.

Don't get me wrong. I did not take it upon myself to make Jordan more "gender aligned." All I did was harmonize his metabolism at my level of awareness and this was the result. This boy was spared unnecessary, painful gender insecurities or conflicts. He was seven and started energy treatments at three!!

Metabolism references the total production and balance of proteins in the body, such as hormones, neurotransmitters, digestive enzymes and acids, immune factors and thousands of the body's critical biochemicals. Doctors ought to be masters in analyzing and harmonizing metabolism, not just drugging the imbalances of it.

Definition of metabolism in the Merriam-Webster dictionary:

Metabolism – is the sum of the processes by which a particular substance is handled in the living body.

"Don't expect things to happen, it's better to feel surprised, than be disappointed.
- Kushandwisdom.tumblr

Chapter 16 - Pink Shade #178

I want to share one of those memorable experiences in my practice that encapsulates the joy I receive from the service to my patients.

Ben, a middle-aged man and a family farmer, has been a chiropractic patient of mine for two decades. He appreciates my advice and the fact that I've gotten him out of more than a few back-pain pickles over the years. Because of this respect, I have been able to talk him into addressing a few of his inflammatory triggers holistically or energetically. So, from time to time, he comes in for a holistic treatment, known as NAET and the SHOW Method. He's had a dozen or so treatments over the years, which have helped to significantly reduce his gout and back pain issues. Recently, he came in after a two-year hiatus with another bout of gout expressing as back pain. At this point, he values my insight about allergies causing all different kinds of back pain episodes, and he agreed to a SHOW treatment (rather than just a chiropractic manipulation of an inflamed back).

What came up for him as a treatment that day was:

- **vegetable fats** (olive oil, canola oil, corn oil, sunflower seed oil, cotton seed oil)

presenting as a metabolic stressor or allergen. We treated this "fat layer" of metabolic issues with combinations:

Digestive enzymes, organs, DNA, hypothalamus and **xanthine oxidase**.

---

*Xanthine Oxidase - Xanthine oxidase synthesizes uric acid and hydrogen peroxide. In gouty people, uric acid can accumulate and precipitate, leading to serious health problems, i.e. arthritis, gout, rheumatism, migraines, heart disease and skin rashes.**(see chapter 8)*

This was a routine SHOW treatment, plus a small chiropractic adjustment.

When he came back the following week for a follow-up visit, I asked him, "How did we make out with that last treatment?" He replied, "It worked" and then smirked. "You know how I know?"

I replied, "How, your back pain is better?"

He said: "Well, yeah, that, but now I can eat mayonnaise without getting diarrhea."

It is moments like this one which keep me going to work every day; my job is entertaining, unpredictable and hugely rewarding.

Now Ben wants me to fix his sleep apnea that he's been diagnosed with. He utters: "I don't want to sleep with a CPAP machine for the rest of my life. Can you help me with this?"

"Well, Ben... potentially," I said. "That will take a bit more effort on your part, and some more SHOW treatments. You'll need to learn breathing exercises, make more changes in your diet to help you lose weight, and maybe even practice yoga."

"I'll do anything," he said. "I'd rather sleep next to my woman than with this machine."

"Sounds like a plan, Ben. The motivation is there. Let's keep moving forward."

"There are more things in heaven and earth, Horatio, than are dreamt of in your philosophy." - *Hamlet*

Chapter 17 – Chronic Subluxation

Karl initially entered my practice on the advice of his wife, a patient at our clinic who had good results with her health issues. At that time, Karl's acute problem was a nagging frontal headache with stuffy sinuses, which hadn't improved over the past two months.

On the initial visit, I energetically detected, with computer scan and MRT a bacterial infection, the common staph and strep type of bacteria, which is what we treated in the first session. Treating, in this case, means applying an energy-specific biofeedback treatment (SHOW Method), allowing me to communicate with and focus the immune system on this variety of bacteria. In the follow-up session and feedback, we focused on a parasite issue. After the first two treatments, Karl's headache was nearly gone.

Because of the way I conduct my routine muscle reflex testing (MRT), I noticed that Karl's right leg was 1¼" shorter than his left. I asked him about it, and he told me that he was already aware, and that he wore a heel lift in all his shoes to compensate for it. He had done this on the advice of his orthopedist <u>and</u> his chiropractor. In other words, Karl had taken care of that problem.

<u>Leg Length check:</u>

Left image shows a balanced and equal leg length.

Right image shows imbalance and positive MRT (functionally short leg).

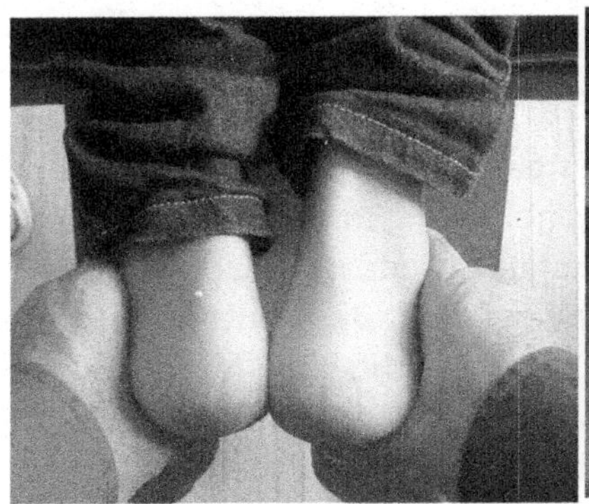

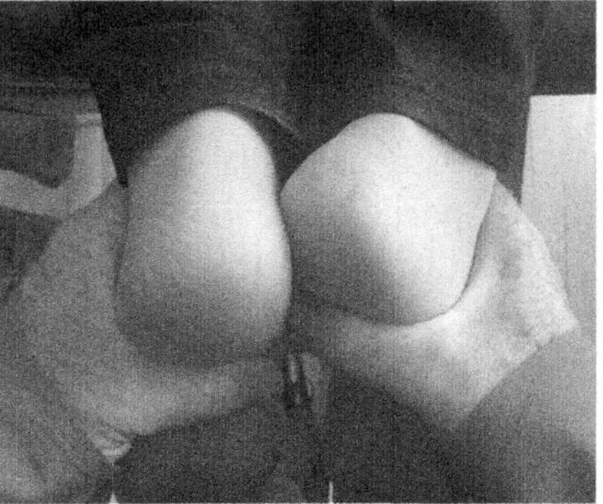

A functionally short leg in chiropractic terms is called 'Pelvic Deficiency' or PD. It is commonly due to a sacroiliac (SI joint) subluxation or a hip or knee subluxation. Therefore, I balanced his leg length, which was more difficult than usual, because it was not just a matter of leveling the pelvis or relaxing the hips, nor even the lumbar spine. The reflexive, muscular component to Karl's leg length discrepancy appeared to be higher up in the spine, at the upper T-spine level.

Why this complication?

Because of an inflammatory process going on somewhere in his upper body, as it soon turned out, because of a Vitamin B 12 'allergy'.

On his third visit, we began working on Karl's metabolic issues, namely food allergies/sensitivities, which were responsible for his weak immune system and allowing multiple lingering/latent infections. Following is the regimen of the next seven visits and respective treatments.

- Treatment # 3 - **Chicken/eggs (poultry/feathers)**
- #4 – **Shellfish**
- #5 - **Vitamin B complex** and **grains**
- #6 - **Spice 1** (phenols from culinary herbs and spices)
- #7 - **Vitamin C and fruit**
- #8 – **Starches**
- #9 – **Yeast**
- #10 - **Fungus**

During these standard desensitization treatments, we modulated his metabolism very specifically, one layer at the time. During this process, I noticed that Karl's right leg length deficiency (shortness) persisted, and I had to remedy this before each session with a chiropractic adjustment. By about the fifth or sixth treatment, I convinced Karl that we had to resolve this issue for real, since it was a functional problem, not an anatomical shortness. As a first step, I asked him to permanently remove the lift from all his shoes, since these lifts were working against us, maintaining the problem, while we were working on permanently *resolving* the problem.

Soon after, Karl had a physical at his MD and he brought in copies of his blood work. I could see some kidney issues and blood lipid issues, but they were marginal. What really grabbed my attention was the "pernicious anemia," which indicated a Vitamin B12 deficiency or a Vitamin B12 metabolic problem.

Pernicious anemia - A decrease in red blood cells when the body can't absorb enough vitamin B-12. Possible complications of pernicious anemia include heart problems, chronic anemia, stomach cancer, and brain and nerve damage. Commonly overlooked symptoms include weakness, headaches and chest pain.

After the first ten treatments, Karl's headaches were completely gone. In that first year, he had a session once a month. We were now responding to acute situations, colds, flu, lower back pain episodes and blood pressure issues. The "short leg" phenomenon was now starting to resolve for a week at a time, but it had always returned by the time I saw Karl again. With the heel lift gone, we had no choice but to plow ahead and harmonize Karl's metabolism and immune system even further, in order to get his pelvis to stay aligned:

- Treatment #11 - **Dairy products**
- #12 - **Wheat/gliadin**
- #13 - **Vitamins A and K**
- #14 - **Vitamin C** (a repeat treatment)
- #15 - **Lipid lipase**

Karl's before and after treatment blood work shows his MCH levels dropping from 33.9 to normal at 31.8.

MCH - High MCH levels can indicate macrocytic anemia, which can be caused by insufficient vitamin B12. Insufficient folic acid can be another cause of macrocytic anemia.

MCH measurement 12/2010: Mean Corpuscular Hemoglobin: 33.9

CBC WITH AUTO DIFF	PROFILE		
WBC	4.8		4.0-10.9
RBC	4.73		4.20-5.40
HEMOGLOBIN	**16.1**	**H**	**12.5-16.0**
HEMATOCRIT	45.4		36.0-47.0
MCV	95.9		80.0-97.0
MCH	**33.9**	**H**	**27.0-31.0**
MCHC	35.4		32.0-36.0
RDW	11.9		11.5-14.5
PLATELET COUNT	212		140-440
NEUTROPHILS	56.5		50-70
LYMPHOCYTES	33.5		20-44
MONOCYTES	6.2		2-9
EOSINOPHIL	3.3		0-4
BASOPHIL	0.5		0-2
ABSOLUTE NEUTROPHILS	2.7		2.05-7.63
ABSOLUTE LYMPHOCYTES	1.6		0.8-4.8
ABSOLUTE MONOCYTES	0.3		0.1-1.0
ABSOLUTE EOSINOPHILS	0.2		0.1-0.5
ABSOLUTE BASOPHILS	0.0		0.0-0.3
HEMATOLOGY COMMENT (COMM2)	N/A		
TSH	1.98		0.34-5.60

MCH measurement 10/2015 – Mean Corpuscular Hemoglobin: 31.8

Test / Profile	Result	H/L	Range
CBC WITH AUTO DIFF	PROFILE		
WBC	5.7		4.1-11.0
RBC	4.75		4.60-6.10
HEMOGLOBIN	15.1		13.5-18.0
HEMATOCRIT	45.2		41.0-53.0
MCV	95.2		80.0-97.0
MCH	31.8		27.0-32.0
MCHC	33.4		32.0-36.0
RDW	12.4		11.5-14.5
PLT Count	197		140-400
Neutrophil	59.8		35.0-75.0
Lymphocyte	30.1		16.0-52.0
Monocyte	6.5		2.0-10.0
Eosinophil	3.0		0.0-5.0
Basophil	0.6		0.0-4.0
Abs Neutrophils	3.4		2.1-8.0
Abs Lymphocytes	1.7		0.8-5.5
ABMON	0.4		0.1-1.0
Abs Eosinophils	0.2		0.0-0.5
Abs Basophils	0.0		0.0-0.3

Karl also had issues with his lipid metabolism. His LDL and cholesterol were fluctuating a lot. If he was very disciplined with his diet and exercise, then his lipids would be okay, but they easily wandered into elevated territory, hence the lipid lipase treatment.

- Treatment #17 - **Vitamin A, Vitamin E and fish** (saltwater fish)
- #18 - **Phenols** of the **pepper spices** and **nightshade vegetables**
- #20 - **Salt** and **beef**

With natural medicines, we were able to address Karl's kidney issues, which included high blood pressure and swollen ankles when he sat for extended periods. This brings us to:

- Treatment #24 – **Aldosterone**

Aldosterone - the main mineralocorticoid hormone, is a steroid hormone produced by the zona glomerulosa of the adrenal cortex in the adrenal gland. It is essential for sodium conservation in the kidney, salivary glands, sweat glands and colon. It plays a central role in the regulation of the plasma sodium (Na+), the extracellular potassium (K+) and arterial blood pressure.

The PD effect was not as rigid as it used to be, but within two weeks or so, it would still recur, despite regular chiropractic adjustments and balancing out the PD at every session in our clinic.

Finally, I told Karl about genetic testing and 23andme, the company providing this service. He agreed to it and completed the test. The raw data of 23andme is huge. I used a few advanced software tools to analyze the results and found some interesting mutations related to his Vitamin B12 metabolism.

The FUT2 and CYP1A2 genes are, among other things, linked to Vitamin B12 dysmetabolism. Also, MTRR showed as a serious mutation, which is involved in the methylation (epigenetic expression) of Vitamin B12 and Folate (Vitamin B9). I performed an advanced SHOW Method treatment/feedback for:

- **Vitamin B12 with FUT2 gene**

And a separate treatment targeting the following 2 groups:

- **cytochrome 450 gene CYP 1A2.**
- **Vitamin B9 (Folate)** and the **gene MTRR.**

What is a gene?

A gene is the basic physical and functional unit of heredity. Genes, which are made up of DNA, act as instructions to make molecules called proteins. In humans, genes vary in size from a few hundred DNA bases to more than 2 million bases.

Interestingly, a few things suddenly fell into place. The PD condition resolved over this two- to three-month session interval. The pernicious anemia problem also finally resolved, as can be seen in the blood work from 10/2015. My kinesiology testing finally allowed for the supplementation of Folate and B12. The reason why initially it didn't allow for supplementation is because it would have only added to Karl's inflammatory issues, since his problem was an inability to metabolize Vitamin B 12.

Homozygous *– We have two copies of most genes we are born with, one from the mother and one from the father. If both copies of a gene are mutated, it's called a homozygous mutation.*

Heterozygous - is the term for one allele (rung of the ladder) being mutated.

Different genes, and there are over 30 000 of them, are more and more combined into functional groups. Depending on which proteins they are encoding.

There are over 8 million possible combinations of 23 chromosome pairs, keeping us all a bit different. Each chromosome contains hundreds of genes. Larger mutations like Cystic Fibrosis involve an entire chromosome. SNPs only affect one gene and are very common. In fact, we all have some SNPs. The different health outcomes for different individuals result from different locations and quantities of SNPs.

Genetic Genie Methylation Profile showing homozygous mutations of MAO gene and MTRR gene:

geneticgenie

Profile: Methylatior
Generated: 4/12/2C

Gene & Variation	rsID	Alleles	Result
COMT V158M	rs4680	AG	+/-
COMT H62H	rs4633	CT	+/-
COMT P199P	rs769224	GG	-/-
VDR Bsm	rs1544410	CT	+/-
VDR Taq	rs731236	AG	+/-
MAO A R297R	rs6323	T	+/+
ACAT1-02	rs3741049	AG	+/-
MTHFR C677T	rs1801133	GG	-/-
MTHFR 03 P39P	rs2066470	GG	-/-
MTHFR A1298C	rs1801131	GT	+/-
MTR A2756G	rs1805087	AA	-/-
MTRR A66G	rs1801394	GG	+/+
MTRR H595Y	not found	n/a	not genotyped
MTRR K350A	rs162036	AA	-/-

Genetic Genie Detox Profile showing homozygous mutation in Cytochrome 450 gene CYP1A2:

Gene & Variation	rsID	Alleles	Result
CYP1A1*2C A4889G	rs1048943	TT	-/-
CYP1A1 m3 T3205C	rs4986883	TT	-/-
CYP1A1 C2453A	rs1799814	GG	-/-
CYP1A2 164A>C	rs762551	CC	+/+
CYP1B1 L432V	rs1056836	CG	+/-
CYP1B1 N453S	rs1800440	CT	+/-
CYP1B1 R48G	rs10012	CG	+/-
CYP2A6*2 1799T>A	rs1801272	AA	-/-
CYP2A6*20	rs28399444	II	-/-
CYP2C9*2 C430T	rs1799853	CT	+/-
CYP2C9*3 A1075C	rs1057910	AA	-/-
CYP2C19*17	rs12248560	CC	-/-
CYP2D6 S486T	rs1135840	CC	-/-
CYP2D6 100C>T	rs1065852	AG	+/-
CYP2D6 2850C>T	rs16947	GG	-/-
CYP2E1*1B 9896C>G	rs2070676	CC	-/-

I am still not entirely sure which organ caused the PD reaction. It may have been the heart or the spleen. The chronic subluxation was located at T 3. In any case, lo and behold, we finally found and remedied this common functional problem by harmonizing, in a precise fashion, Vitamin B12 and folate (B 9) metabolism.

The connection between physical manifestation (short leg/PD) and functional expression (unhealthy blood/elevated MCH) was established and resolved. The crutch of ignorance, the heel lift, was tossed into the trashcan and better health on many different levels was finally possible. Even though this issue took the better part of two years to accomplish, the health benefits over his lifetime will be immeasurable.

After all, isn't that why we go to the doctor in the first place? To get help in RESOLVING our health issues. To seek out help in healing our bodies. Sometimes, the form of that healing may not be what we expect, but it is essential that we continue exploring our options beyond what the health insurance system is going to cover!

The notion that we can address every issue with medication, or a surgical intervention is futile. Working at the energetic level of life opens an entire new world that can lead us to much better prevention, outcomes and awareness. Also, since energy medicine in my context of the SHOW Method includes epigenetic function and mutations, it has positive influences on future generations – our own children and grandchildren.

Unfortunately, there is the problem of accessibility. While the cost of these kind of treatments is low compared to medical, palliative care, they are cash only and not covered by insurance. This cuts out probably more than half of the population from pursuing this alternative.

"Whenever we proceed from the known into the unknown we may hope to understand, but we may have to learn at the same time a new meaning of the word 'understanding." *– Werner Heisenberg, Physics and Philosophy, The Revolution in Modern Science*

Chapter 18 – Peanut Anaphylaxis

The first time he came to our clinic, Kyle was 10 years old. With his red hair and freckles, he reminded me a bit of Richie Cunningham (Ron Howard) in Happy Days. Just a lot less Los Angeles and much more of a country boy, living in CNY; more comfortable exploring the woods than spending time in a doctor's office. His Mom had told us of a lifelong Peanut Anaphylaxis. During his childhood he and his parents had made many scary trips to the ER. He lived with an EpiPen at all times, which means, his family carried with them an EpiPen wherever they went.

The number of children in the US with a peanut allergy has more than tripled between 1997 and 2008. Why? Good question! Something has changed in our kids. Certainly, they have received many more vaccines than previous generations and our food supply is being sprayed with chemicals more than ever, just to mention a few of the culprits.

Kyle had a bunch of other allergies which affected his breathing when he contracted a cold for example. Something which happened quite frequently. As always in these situations, Kyle's immune system was weak and not functioning optimally at all. His Immune System was handicapped by all his allergies. He was sick a lot.

We did not have any time to waste; a lot of work needed to be done on him so, we started immediately.

As a rule, with anaphylaxis treatments, I never touch the monster itself in the beginning. No, peanuts themselves we would not treat until the 15th treatment. There are many constituents to peanuts, each one which could present digestive trouble triggering allergic reactions:

Oils (oleic and Linoleic acids), lots of protein, many minerals such as Magnesium, Iron, Potassium, Copper, Manganese and Molybdenum. Many Vitamins like Vitamin B 1, 3, 9 (Folic Acid), Biotin, and Vitamin E as well as sugars.

It was therefore not surprising, that the first few treatments were not directly related to peanuts. SHOW Method treatment #1:

- **Vitamin C**

Followed right away by our first immune focus, treatment #2:

- **Parasites / intestinal**

Turned out that Kyle was bruising easily, a red flag for Vitamin C deficiency. In his case a result of a Vitamin C allergy, which scientifically we call a metabolic dysfunction of Vitamin C.

This "little" detail improved right away; his bruising became normal.

We could now move on to other treatments:

- **Sugars**
- **Pollen**

This brought about more energy for Kyle. Next up:

- **Yeast / Candida**
- **Vitamin B Complex**

At the next visit Kyle complained about stuffy sinuses. These groups of immune and metabolic or allergic issues were treated in the following treatment segment over the next month:

- **Staph** and **Strep Bacteria** (immune focus)
- **Vitamin B Complex** and **MTHFR mutation**
- **Grains** and **MTHFR mutation**
- **Eggs** and **MTHFR mutation**

Kyle's sinus congestion continued to be a concern and we had to work on immune function with an emphasis on bacteria besides the "routine" food allergies.

- **Minerals** and **MTHFR**
- **Staph** and **Strep Bacteria**

Kyle's sinusitis finally resolved, without Antibiotics. Some weeks later we continued treatments with these issues of dysmetabolism or food allergies:

- **Vitamin K**
- **Calcium**
- **Tree Nuts**
- **Vitamin A**

About 3 months into this process, we finally treated fats and oils, which was probably a major issue in the peanut anaphylaxis:

- **Peanut Oil**
- **Soybean Oil** and **Palm Oil**
- **Legumes (Dried Beans) –** peanuts are part of the legume family
- **Salt**
- **Staph** and **Strep Bacteria**

His next appointment came about 5 months into this treatment regimen. This time, I put some peanut butter onto Kyle's forearm, to observe his reaction to the real thing. Not wanting to miss anything at this stage, I watched him closely; monitoring his heart rate with an oximeter. His anxious mother did the same. Nothing happened, he was fine.

We watched him closely for 3 minutes and everything was just fine, I thoroughly washed off the peanut butter and performed a SHOW Method treatment on an acute issue:

- **West Nile Virus**

West Nile Virus – spread by mosquitos.
Common even in Central New York.

At the end of this confidence building experiment of peanuts on Kyle, we continued with the many remaining issues at hand:

- **Tree Pollen** and **Berries**
- **Fabrics** (mix of common fabrics, incl. cotton, spandex)

On this day he was just coming back from a camping vacation, and his immune system needed to be boosted yet again:

- **Staph** and **Strep Bacteria**

Finally, nine months and 14 treatments into it, we treated peanuts themselves, in combination with Hormones (Cortisol and Epinephrine or Adrenalin) and Zonulin:

- **Peanuts** and **Walnuts / Hormones** and **Zonulin**

  All in one combination treatment.

Zonulin – an intestinal flora functioning as a physiologic modulator of intercellular Tight Junctions. The discovery of Zonulin has led us to appreciate that its up-regulation in genetically susceptible individuals leads to autoimmune diseases.

Kyle's blood work for allergies did show a level 3 allergy to Walnuts. Also, a level 3 allergy to Eggs which we treated on visit # 6. The egg allergy had harmonized quite nicely, which could be seen from his yearly allergy blood work.

However, our work wasn't done yet. Not so much because peanuts still showed up as an allergy level 4 in his blood work, but because more allergies still existed and had to be eliminated or harmonized. In other words, Kyle still had more mutations to overcome and improve his metabolism functionally and epigenetically. His genetic expression in dealing with the environment still needed improvement.

Another aspect we had to pay attention to was rehabilitation of the weakest organ systems. This is done with nutritional support.

Kyle's two weakest systems were his adrenal glands and his Digestive System including his Microbiome. He took an adrenal glandular product to support rehabilitation of his adrenals and Probiotics supplementation (in an empty stomach) to improve his Biome and intestinal wall integrity.

__Adrenal glands__ produce hormones that help regulate your metabolism, immune system, blood pressure, response to stress and other essential functions.

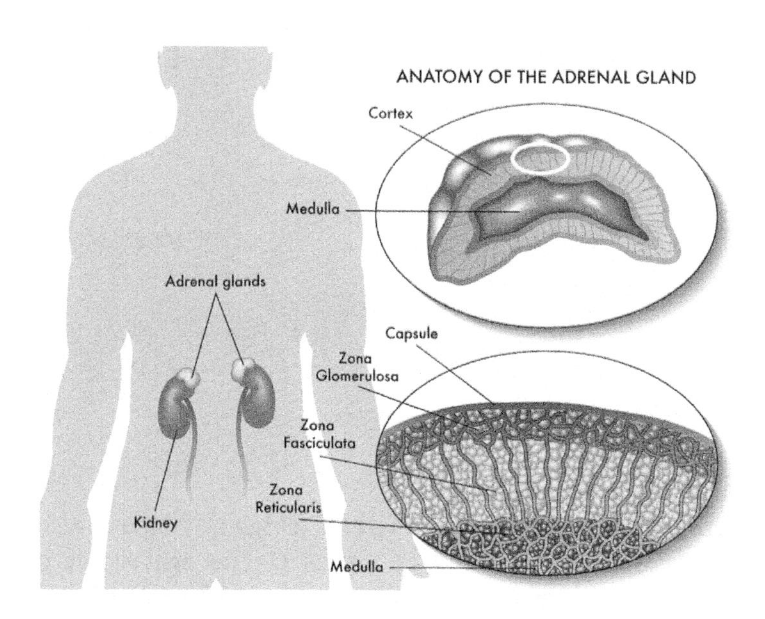

OK, a bit more work to be done:

- **Iron**
- **MTHFR A1268C mutation / variant**
- **Vitamin B 5**
- **Yeast/Candida**
- **Fungus** and **Molds**

Kyle wasn't the first kid I would be treating for peanut anaphylaxis. The biggest challenge I always encounter is getting them to try a tiny amount of peanut butter; to consciously ingest peanut butter.

These kids are so scared of peanuts, because it caused them multiple near-death experiences. They are petrified of peanuts. So are the parents. With anaphylaxis, I carefully monitor those kids' progress and very gently expose them to peanut butter in the office. And, over time, increase their confidence and trust in their own bodies. I finally got Kyle to put his tongue onto a spoon of peanut butter and just touch it, very quickly for the first time. On another day and at a different time, maybe he'll touch the peanut butter for a full second.

It went well with Kyle. But he is still no friend of peanuts. So deep seated is the fear of peanuts. But Kyle is only 12 now, plenty of time to heal, heal body and mind.

Meanwhile he comes to the clinic for any immune or sensitivity issues arising in everyday life. Each visit we treat and harmonize another layer of his metabolism, his immune system or really his genetic expression. Some of those follow-ups were:

- **Dust**
- **Flu Viruses**
- **Shell Fish**
- **Cold Viruses**

With his experience, Kyle will grow up to pursue his good health by healing himself energetically, becoming conscious of his epigenetic shortfalls and nutritionally support his needy tissues. He will probably reserve pharmaceutical intervention to true emergencies and real medical situations.

Kyle's case was not just with peanuts; he had a slew of allergies and immune weakness. And, to permanently rid him of his peanut anaphylaxis, we had to heal his gut and harmonize his genetic expression in a precise manner by addressing dozens of allergies and sensitivities.

The MTHFR genetic imbalance appeared to play a centre role. We never completed any genetic testing with Kyle, but between the computer scans and the MRT (Muscle Reflex Testing) it was very convincing to be a major problem to resolve.

Kyle is on no medications, he does not take any supplements permanently. He is just living independently, healthy. No more sitting at "the peanut table" in school.

"What seems to us as bitter trials are often Blessings in disguise." - *Oscar Wilde*

Chapter 19 – Shingles

Ariana came to our clinic referred by a regional Integrative Health Center. One of the MDs there had heard about the work we do with allergies and felt the compassion to refer her to us. Ariana's stated health goal upon entry to our clinic was "to overcome her chemical sensitivities", which made her life miserable.

Ariana had a Lyme doctor who she's been seeing regularly for over 4 years. Apparently, the Lyme was still going on, however the specialist MD already worked on that problem. She also had a Mold/Fungus doctor who she's been seeing for over a year for an apparent Valley Fever infection. Another specialist in their field, yet the Valley Fever infection supposedly was still ongoing. Ariana had many other diagnoses, like hypothyroid – even though she was thin as a rail, looking more like hyperthyroid. Oh yes, and she had a Detox doctor, specifically to organize her detoxification regimens. So, another issue I didn't have to worry about, detoxification was already handled by an alternative specialist. Ariana was very fond of her. All I was expected to do was, get rid of Ariana's chemical sensitivities. No less, no more, and if successful, that would have made me yet another star in Ariana's healthcare team.

Ariana was a go getter, at 47 years of age, she wanted to be active in her family businesses and be the matriarch she needed to be. For that reason, she was an ideal patient for me, motivated to do whatever it takes to get well. As you will see from her story, it takes motivation, patience, courage and perseverance to work through these life cycles and health challenges.

Somewhere, buried in Ariana's health history was a "spontaneous pneumothorax" 29 years ago, when she was a young woman. This event climaxed with a surgically removed rib that caused unexplainable pain. Of course, the removal of the rib did not resolve the pain in the upper backside. She lived with this rather uncomfortable pain for 29 years.

Ariana had gone through many rounds of every Antibiotic known to man, in the past 4 years particularly, including IV (intra-venous). She even had a Picc line for a while, so she could receive her IV antibiotic treatments outpatient.

Lately she was on antifungals by her 'Valley Fever' doctor as well. She could find no relief. She was in bad shape when she arrived at our clinic. Well, we better get to work. Sounds like there are a FEW problems to resolve.

The first three months Ariana came twice a week for treatments, then once a week for 3 months. All were SHOW Method treatments. Txt #1:

- **Yeast/Candida**

and a three times higher dose of Probiotics she was presently taking. Stopping or changing all the well-intentioned but unsuccessful supplementation protocols from the many other practitioners proofed to be the most challenging part of Ariana's treatment protocol and full recovery. We had 7 months ahead of us. Treatment #2 and #3:

- **Sugars**
- **Pollen**

And then the first infection presented:

- **Bartonella**

The **Bartonella** was to present the biggest challenge in eliminating completely. It took some 6 months of vigilance to escort the last Bartonella out of Ariana's body.

***Bartonella** - bacteria that are known to be carried by fleas, body lice and ticks, and there's high suspicion that ticks transmit it to humans. People with tick bites and no known exposure to cats have acquired the disease. People who recall being bitten by ticks have been co-infected with the Lyme spirochete and Bartonella. Traditionally causes cat scratch fever.*

Right away I employed Bromelain, a proteolytic enzyme, to remove the **Biofilm** off the Bartonella in order to expose the nasty bacteria to the Immune System. Now the Immune System may recognize the Bartonella and then will be able to eliminate it. Since there are no good medical solutions for Bartonella, this is a real good thing. Your own Immune System getting rid of an infection. Awesome

Continuing to harmonize Ariana's metabolism, in order to reduce inflammation and strengthen her Immune System, we treated:

- **Eggs / Chicken**

And look who showed up:

- **Lyme / Borrelia Burgdorferi**

Biofilm *- Acute infections are assumed to involve planktonic bacteria, which are generally treatable with antibiotics, although successful treatment depends on accurate and fast diagnosis. However, in cases where the bacteria succeed in forming a biofilm within the human host, the infection often turns out to be untreatable and will develop into a chronic state. The important hallmarks of chronic biofilm-based infections are extreme resistance to antibiotics and many other conventional antimicrobial agents, and an extreme capacity for evading the host defenses. (App 13)*

Didn't take that long, just about 5 treatments or so into the effort. Whether the Lyme showed up in the IMAET scan or if, out of curiosity I checked the vial, I don't recall. The energy (frequency) of Lyme reacted, and we started to focus the Immune System on Borrelia. In addition to the SHOW Method treatment for Lyme, I added Olive Leaf Extract as an anti-bacterial medicine to be taken 3 times a day at home.

Next Treatment:

- **Salt**

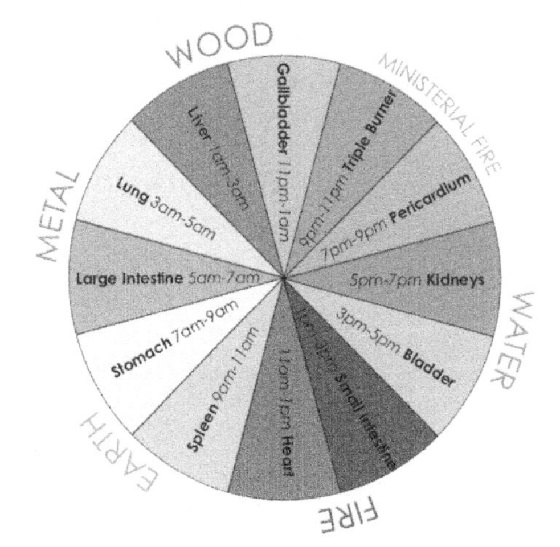

Ariana complaint about itchy skin and some Herxheimer reactions with the Olive Leaf Extract supplement. She expressed it as "it makes me feel crappy". She is waking up at 2 am with difficulty falling back to sleep. According to TCM, 2 am is smack in the middle of the Liver restoration period, which is an indication of liver stress. The liver is also the main detoxification organ and Ariana has big detoxification difficulties.

It only makes sense that nutritionally we want to support the liver in a big way. Simply rehabilitating the liver with effective natural medicine support. In this case I used a powerful Chinese herb formula called Brown Juice. (App 14) It features ancient Chinese Medicine knowledge combined with modern herbal delivery techniques.

Soon we would be harmonizing her mutated genes in her detox profile for the ultimate liver rehabilitation.

Ariana always researched the things we treated and talked with me and staff about her findings as well as other ideas. This day she was wondering if she had a problem with aldehydes. They seem to make her "feel crappy". Sure enough, she had problems with the entire Aldehyde group (layer):

- **Aldehydes, Formaldehyde, Acetaldehyde**

And the first gene or mutation came up for her in this context to harmonize:

- **ADH (Aldehyde dehydrogenase)**

Alcohol brakes down into aldehydes and aldehydes are in many perfumes and essential oils.

__ADH__ – Aldehyde dehydrogenase is a group of __enzymes__ that __catalyze__ the __oxidation__ of __aldehydes__. Despite the name "__dehydrogenase__", their mode of oxidation is by addition of oxygen rather than by removal of hydrogen – that is, they convert aldehydes to __carboxylic acids__. To date, nineteen ALDH genes have been identified within the human genome. These genes participate in a wide variety of biological processes including the detoxification of exogenously and endogenously generated aldehydes. These enzymes are found in many tissues of the body but are at the highest concentration in the liver.

Well, it was no surprise to find this, because Ariana could not drink any amount of alcohol and was highly allergic to perfumes and aromatics

.

Look at Ariana's Detox Profile: She has five homozygous mutations within those detox genes. The ultimate reason for her environmental sensitivities.

Detox Profile – Genetic Genie:

CYP1A1*2C A4889G	rs1048943	TT	-/-
CYP1A1 m3 T3205C	rs4986883	TT	-/-
CYP1A1 C2453A	rs1799814	GG	-/-
CYP1A2 164A>C	rs762551	CC	+/+
CYP1B1 L432V	rs1056836	GG	+/+
CYP1B1 N453S	rs1800440	TT	-/-
CYP1B1 R48G	rs10012	CC	+/+
CYP2A6*2 1799T>A	rs1801272	AA	-/-
CYP2A6*20	rs28399444	II	-/-
CYP2C9*2 C430T	rs1799853	CC	-/-
CYP2C9*3 A1075C	rs1057910	AC	+/-
CYP2C19*17	rs12248560	CC	-/-
CYP2D6 S486T	rs1135840	GG	+/+
CYP2D6 100C>T	rs1065852	AG	+/-
CYP2D6 2850C>T	rs16947	AG	+/-
CYP2E1*1B 9896C>G	rs2070676	CG	+/-
CYP2E1*1B 10023G>A	rs55897648	GG	-/-
CYP2E1*4 4768G>A	rs6413419	GG	-/-
CYP3A4*1B	rs2740574	TT	-/-
CYP3A4*2 S222P	rs55785340	AA	-/-
CYP3A4*3 M445T	rs4986910	AA	-/-
CYP3A4*16 T185S	rs12721627	GG	-/-
GSTP1 I105V	rs1695	GG	+/+

And one can improve genetic issues like these?

According to my clinical experience and many testimonial feedbacks from patients, absolutely. There are limits to anyone's toxic load. Dosage is everything. But detoxification can be improved with SHOW Method treatments at the epigenetic level. Ariana couldn't touch a glass of wine for decades. She had real symptoms around people wearing perfumes. Formaldehyde, which is everywhere in our environment; carpets, furniture, building materials, it is even in certain vaccinations, was a real problem for her. We certainly desensitized her to some of these chemicals or increased her tolerance of them. (by increasing detoxification capacity) See the chapter "Side effects from Pharmaceutical Medicines"

The next treatment just 'washed up' a variety of co-infections. We simply did a SHOW treatment with an Immune focus:

- **Leishmania brazil & Babesia diversi**

Of course, we encountered some setbacks and pitfalls along the way. For example, at this stage I muscle tested Ariana for GABA (she must have complained about anxiety or something of that nature) and she tested that she needed it. So, I gave her the supplement with great anticipation. At the next appointment she reported "it made me feel like I was run over by a truck". It turned out that she was allergic to GABA and we had to resolve that detail by harmonizing the GAD gene:

- **GAD** (Glutamate decarboxylase)

GAD - GAD1 is a gene that produces GAD67. This enzyme breaks down the anxiety inducing neurotransmitter ***glutamate*** *into calming neurotransmitter* ***GABA****. GAD catalyzes the production of GABA.*

After this little, eye opening bump, we continued treatments:

- **Iron / red meat**
- **Calcium**

- **Grains**

We now were 10 treatments and 5 weeks into this process and progress in feeling better was slow. However, progress in harmonizing the underlying metabolic issues was significant. There is no way around it, these metabolic issues are genomic stressors such as mutations and are at the root of most immune deficiencies as well as chemical sensitivities.

Headaches would frequently accompany Ariana's physical discomforts, as it did on this appointment. Here is visit # 11:

- **EBV** (Epstein Barr Virus)

Remember the hypothyroid history! Chronic EBV infections are a known hidden cause of Hypothyroidism. Moving on:

- **Nightshade vegetables / Peppers**

Ariana went through so many stages of Herxheimer reactions and detox struggles. At this stage her Blood pressure dropped below 60 and we had to lower the dose of Olive Leaf Extract.

For the first time some of Ariana's chemical sensitivities could be worked on, as determined by muscle testing and IMAET scan.

- **Sulfanilamide, Sulfur dioxide**
- **Food Preservatives**
- **Tree Nuts**

Meanwhile Ariana had some blood work done with her Medical Doctor and for the first time in 4 years her WBC count (White Blood Cell) was normal. Nice. There is hope she might be feeling better as well, soon. We soldiered on:

- **Vitamin C**
- **Tree Pollen**
- **Bartonella**

The Bartonella issue was not resolved 100%. It showed up again and right away I reinforced the Bromelain regimen at 2 capsules twice a day, not a terribly high dose. But one had to tread carefully with Ariana. We did some more work:

- **Wheat and Gliadin**
- **Grasses**

All along this journey, Ariana had taken Iodine of a super high dose on the direction of her Functional doctor. Even though it gave her a rash, she would not stop. Finally, it was time to treat her Iodine allergy:

- **Iodine**

Ariana had called the office reporting that she was retaining fluid in her legs. At the next appointment a common bacterial infection transpired. We did an Immune treatment with a focus on:

- **Staph / Strep Bacteria**

GPCR - the G protein-coupled receptor gene superfamily consists of hundreds of members that are widely expressed in all tissues and serve as receptors for a diverse complement of ligands.

- **GCPR** (G-protein coupled receptor)

As we struggled through this difficult time, headaches were a serious complication, Ariana had an emergency biofeedback session which revealed brain issues and particularly brain trauma. At this session she revealed that she had 2 years of ECT treatments (Electroconvulsive therapy) earlier in her life. I don't even remember what for. Just the thought of it made me cringe. We had yet some work ahead: Over the next 3 visits we treated:

- **Animal Fat**
- **Corn**
- **DHEA** (Dehydroepiandrosterone)

DHEA – is a steroidal hormone produced mostly in the adrenals. It modulates a variety of pathways throughout the body involved in various aspects of health and disease via direct actions independent of its role as a precursor to androgens (sex hormones).

Ariana just didn't feel well yet. She reported horrible headaches, right sided facial headaches, night sweats and insomnia. It was a struggle. I thought for sure she was going to quit. But Ariana could tell her body was changing and she hung in there. We came back to, 'surprise, surprise':

- **Lyme / Borrelia**
- **Bartonella**
- **CYP 2E1** (Cytochrome 450 gene segment)

Cytochrome 2E1 - Metabolizes several pre-carcinogens, drugs, and solvents to reactive metabolites. Inactivates many drugs and xenobiotics and bioactivates many xenobiotic substrates to their hepatotoxic or carcinogenic forms.

This treatment of the detox gene CYP 2E1, brought about the first significant improvement in Ariana's overall feeling. She was relieved in significantly feeling better. However, no respite yet. We had to press on. The next treatments brought out a familiar fellow:

- **Bartonella**
- **CYP 2E1**
- **Legumes**

For the first time during this regimen of treatments, about 20 now, Ariana reported of "feeling really good". She slept better. I was breathing a sigh of relief. At last we had turned the corner. We now treated once a week.

- **Bartonella**
- **MTHFR A1298**
- **Hay fever**

Yes, hay fever. It was the end of July after all. Ariana reported feeling better each visit. But she wasn't out of the woods yet entirely.

- **Vitamin A / Fish**
- **Lactose**
- **Perfumes**
- **MAO**

MAO gene -(Monoamine oxidase)
has earned the nickname "warrior gene" because it has been linked to aggression in observational and survey-based studies. More importantly it encodes mitochondrial enzymes which catalyze the oxidative deamination of amines, such as dopamine, norepinephrine, and serotonin.

- **MTHFR A1298**

More 'stuff' to treat: At this point it feels laborious, but the results of 'feeling better' provide the motivation to go to the 'Finish'.

- **Gelatin**
- **Glycine**
- **Casein**
- **Collagen**

At this appointment, Ariana reported, that after eating peanut butter she got a headache, her chest tightened up and she had difficulty breathing. Her energy scans revealed, and we treated:

- **Lectins / peanuts / wheat / peppers**

HLA DQ8 - There are many different types of the HLA-DQ genes of which DQ2 and DQ8 are only two. As a group, their main function is to help the body identify agents that may be harmful, allowing the immune system to target those cells for neutralization. Every one of us has two copies of an HLA-DQ serotype, one which we inherit from our mother and the other which we inherit from our father. If faulty this gene has been identified in Gluten intolerance.

- **HLA DQ8**

And just like a bad penny, here shows up the stubborn Bartonella yet again:

- **Bartonella**

All through Ariana's treatment regimen, we had to focus her Immune System on the Bartonella infection consistently, whenever it presented.

So, Ariana still had some less than perfect weeks in between appointments. This week she reported that taking Vitamin D makes her depressed. Well that's not good. A little MRT testing showed we had to treat:

- **Vitamin D / VDR** (Vitamin D Receptor)

That took care of that little problem. Some more genetic detox problems surfaced and were corroborated by 23andme test results:

- **CYP 2D6** (Cytochrome 450 gene component)

We were now completing our 30th treatment and Ariana felt 90% better. Occasionally a symptom will show up exposing yet another genomic issue. More co-infections and auto-immune issues:

- **Mycoplasma**
- **HLA DQ8** (repeat treatment)

All along this intense 5-month treatment period, Ariana mentioned a few times, that she had this significant rib pain, center of the right shoulder blade. But she had it for 29 years and it was just like another headache. Something she had learned to live with. Except now, that all the other issues appeared somewhat settled, this old nagging pain became a real bother.

The story goes that 29 years ago, after a "spontaneous" pneumothorax, the pain was so debilitating, that a piece of rib 4 was surgically removed. I have no idea why? Presumably because it hurt. Remove the part that hurts, problem solved; right?! Of course, that did not solve the problem. And Ariana has been living with this pain for 29 years.

So, on visit # 32, doesn't Herpes Zoster and Varicella Zoster show up in the IMAET scan. A light bulb went off in my head. Could that chronic rib pain on the right side, close to the spine, be shingles?

No way. That's just not reasonably possibly. 29 years, dozens of doctors, literally hundreds of tests ....

Shingles - is an infection caused by the varicella-zoster virus, which is the same virus that causes ***chickenpox****. Even after the chickenpox infection is over, the virus may live in your* ***nervous system*** *for years before reactivating as shingles. Shingles may also be referred to as herpes zoster. Most cases of shingles clear up within two to three weeks. Shingles rarely occurs more than once in the same person, but approximately* ***1 in 3 people in the United States*** *will have shingles at some point in their life, according to the Centers for Disease Control and Prevention.*

Luckily, since Ariana's other symptoms were more than 90% resolved, I could actually ponder this crazy possibility that for 29 years everyone had failed to recognize that shingles may be the culprit of this chronic rib pain. No way, impossible. All these doctors back then and since, all missed that this could be due to shingles. I guess, because it occurred without the traditional rash.

So, I carefully sorted out this shingles "angle" and sure enough, all my shingles vials, chicken pox and Varicella Herpes Virus reacted per MRT (Muscle Reflex Technique) or kinesiology. I always double check on the software results if it's something odd, like this finding.

We did this series of 5 treatments over the next 5 weeks:

- **Herpes Zoster / Varicella Virus**
- **CYP 1B1** (another cytochrome 450 gene component, responsible for phase 1 detoxification)

- **Herpes Zoster (shingles)**
- **SOD2 (Superoxide dismutase)**
- **Herpes Zoster / Varicella**

SOD2 - (also called Manganese dependent SOD) transforms superoxide produced by your mitochondria into the less toxic hydrogen peroxide and oxygen. This function allows SOD2 to clear mitochondrial reactive oxygen species (ROS) and confer protection against cell death.

Low and behold, the "29-year-old" pain reduced significantly. We had to do a couple of more "touch up" treatments:

- **Interleukin-2 / HBB gene**
- **Varicella Zoster / NOS** (Nitric Oxide Synthase)

Finally, Ariana's rib pain around the center shoulder blade, which had tortured her for 29 years, went away entirely during the course of these handful of treatments.

First her Immune System had to get rid of Bartonella and Lyme, then the chronic Epstein Barr Virus and a few other co-infections, when in due time, her Immune System was ready to tackle a very old, chronic and odd shingles case. And it happened rather quickly, because by this time we had eliminated many allergies, harmonized many genetic variants (SNPs), many related to detoxification, and in turn strengthened her Immune System significantly.

A metabolism riddled with allergies cannot produce a strong immune response. A metabolism pre-occupied with generating inflammation is going to neglect real immune function. In my experience, allergies and immune weakness go hand in hand. They therefor have to be treated simultaneously.

We did just that with Ariana rather tediously.

While Ariana was not the simplest case nor the easiest patient I ever had, a couple of qualities made her treatment protocol successful: She was willing to do whatever it took. She didn't give up when a healing crisis made life temporarily even worse. And she didn't throw in the towel when we had to work through setbacks, which are inevitable when you work in uncharted territory like we did. In the end it took 7 months to accomplish all that we did, and, in the process, we identified her genetic weakness in the detoxification pathways, which was responsible for her chemical sensitivities. But we didn't just identify them, we harmonized them with resonating SHOW Method treatments. A process which appears to upregulate epigenetic function of the targeted genes, presumably through resonation. And that in return, increases the capacity to detoxify, from within. Which really just means at the cellular level, where life happens.

Difficulties detoxifying the debris from the elimination of all the pathogens caused many of Ariana's unpleasant episodes. Uncovering the many chronic infections exposed Ariana's weak genetic links in the detoxification pathways. Chemical sensitivities are due to detoxification difficulties. I had a concept on how to harmonize those genetic shortcomings and Ariana has significant fewer chemical sensitivities now.

Ariana is quite happy today.

"Surprises are all part of life's journey." - *unknown*

Chapter 20 - Tourette's / Tic Disorder

5-year-old Franky, a lively Kindergartener, is referred to our clinic by a family friend. He suffers from a Tic disorder that manifests in vocal tics and body tics. The body tics are like mini seizures. They are quite frequent, all through the day and have been going on for over one year. Franky is a very normal kid, looks healthy, busy with school activities, including gymnastics. There's just one little problem, he's developed this Tic disorder. And they are increasing in frequency. And yes, there is one other seemingly harmless inconvenience, Franky also deals with regular constipation.

Franky's parents are quite concerned. They have taken him to many doctors, including the regional Neurology Center. Different workups, no results.

The common Tourette's treatments are various psychotropic pharmaceuticals, which have serious side effects. Franky's condition was determined to not require medication at this time. No advice, no strategy on how to overcome this frightening condition.

I considered it a stroke of good luck, that he was not put on anti-convulsive drugs or psychotropic drugs to suppress the tics, because it always adds a layer of complication to my job, resolving the dysfunction. Patients have been thoroughly frightened into taken these drugs and it takes a good amount of courage from the parents or collaboration from the prescribing MD to discontinue the medications.

These days, with many health concerns, including neurological ones, a gluten-free diet is often suggested. Not in this case. And, in most cases, not necessary with the SHOW Method. We'll fix that too, if gluten turns out to be a problem. So, with no solution offered and no strategy in moving forward, here is Franky in my office.

Because he is only 5 years old, this should be "easy". Right?! The younger we get to harmonize genetic expression on an individual, the quicker the results, the longer the life-long benefits of improved epigenetic function.

Luckily, I don't have to do any physical exams, no workups, it's all been done repeatedly. There are only two problems with Franky, chronic constipation and moderate Tourette's. So, we go straight to our energy work:

SHOW Method treatment # 1:

- **Poxviruses**

  In combination with: **Vitamin B Complex.**

Where the pox viruses came from is unclear. Could be acute, but more likely from a vaccination. Next, we harmonized:

- **Sugars** and **Pollen**

  In combination with **CYP 2E1** (see page 114)

- **Tree Nuts**

  In combination with **Bacteria Enterococcinum** and **Nrf2 gene**

Nrf2 gene – functions as a major mechanism in the cellular defense against oxidative stress. Its action is activation of the Nrf2-antioxidant response element signaling pathway, which controls the expression of genes whose protein products are involved in the detoxication and elimination of reactive oxidants (Free Radicals) through conjugative reactions and by enhancing cellular antioxidant capacity.

Franky's Tics were already improving. They were significantly less frequent. Awesome.

SHOW Method treatment # 4:

- **Grains and Gluten**

  With combination **Xanthine Oxidase** (see page 67)

I put Franky on a Probiotic supplement, to be taken twice a day in an empty stomach. This is to support his Microbiome and improve the integrity of his intestinal mucosa.

Franky was on a once a week treatment schedule. After this visit (#4) the stomach doesn't hurt any longer, the constipation dissipates. The tics are gone for 5 days. Just yesterday he experienced a couple of Tics. OK, we're not quite finished yet.

Treatment # 5:

- **Vitamin B5** (Pantothenic Acid)

  In combination with **SOX 10 gene**

---

*Attaching to critical regions near genes, SOX proteins help control the activity of those genes. SOX **proteins** are called transcription factors on the basis of this action.*
SOX10 protein is essential for the formation of nerves in the intestine (enteric nerves) and for the production of specialized cells called melanocytes.

After treatment # 5, the tics are gone. For a full week anyway. So, let's see if we can extend that to 2 weeks.

- **Vitamin C** and **Tree Pollen**

Bingo, the tics are not coming back. Gone, disappeared.

No dietary restrictions, no medications. Only a Probiotic and six SHOW Method energy treatments, and, the scary tics are history.

Well, life goes on. Franky is in a good position to continue his childhood development. If a health issue arises, his mother will bring him back and we'll resolve that issue the same way. Remember we all have thousands of mutations and SNPs, leaving us vulnerable. But you now know, there is a natural method to harmonize many of these pesky little quirks in our God given DNA.

Healthcare becomes a lifestyle choice. GOD gave us an amazingly versatile and capable set of genes. Genes which have been tested for survival over thousands of years. So why would we not be able to live naturally any longer?

We have the scientific, modern knowledge and the proven, ancient traditions to live and survive naturally. Let's keep researching these applications and bringing them to the mainstream and into the public healthcare arena.

This is not to diminish the medical model. Thankfully, for emergencies, we have our medical interventions. Thankfully. We are very blessed to have access to incredible advances in medicine.

But I do feel and observe, that our present healthcare system is over-utilizing the medical system, relying way too much on drugs for common health issues, while neglecting and often suppressing natural, drug-free methods. There has been a lot of progress in natural and alternative techniques as well. We need to put this knowledge, old and new, to smart use.

"Miracles come in moments. Be ready and willing." - *Wayne Dyer*

Chapter 21 – Tension Headaches

Jack was referred by a friend who works out at the same gym as he does. He is a quintessential stud, just past 40. Just past a divorce. Evidently not without scars. A young man who grew up on a farm, now working in construction. A young man working with his hands, but quite smart and with good instincts.

Jack had some sort of a car accident some two and a half years ago. And while he had occasional headaches all his life, ever since this car accident, the headaches appear to become more frequent. The past year almost daily. They hit sort of in back of the head, feel like they are coming up from the neck. He described them as tension headaches.

Jack has seen a chiropractor. He has tried meds prescribed by his Medical Doctor. But the headaches are getting worse and more frequent. So, here he is, in my office, sent by a fellow CrossFit enthusiast.

What is there to do?! No time to waste, we get to work.

It happened to be Pollen season in late spring and so we started, after some kinesiology testing with:

- **Sugars** and **Springtime Pollen**.

Guess what. Low and behold, when he comes back the next week, the headaches are gone. Wow, that was a pleasant outcome. And quick.

We followed up with another treatment anyhow, since there are most likely other little metabolic quirks lurking in his body causing havoc called inflammation. Treatment # 2:

- **Vitamin C** and **Tree Pollen**

Tree Pollen are different from Springtime Pollen in that they are constituently related to Vitamin C rather than to sugars.

The headaches never did come back. And we were now working on some other inflammatory issues, which Jack never even thought about changing. Little things which didn't bother him that much, like occasional low back pain. And so, he did a couple more treatments for good measure, because by now he was pretty impressed with my doctoring.

He knew Gluten didn't agree with him very well, but a gluten-free diet in the past didn't feel right and so when Gluten came up, he was all for resolving that issue as well.

- **Grains** and **Gluten**
- **Herpes Simplex I**

Jack did have a tendency to show up to his appointments dehydrated. A little counseling on that issue fell on receptive ears.

In the end, I believe, the car accident had little to do with his headaches. They could have been a trigger on top of his metabolic or genomic short comings. One category of which are just simple allergies, often caused by SNPs and genetic variants.

The fact is, we all have these SNPs to various degrees. They are just spread differently across our individual genomes, therefor causing different health issues.

Jack's case demonstrated the SHOW Method at its best. This is the kind of healthcare **we, the people**, need.

"An optimist sees the opportunity in every difficulty." *- Winston Churchill*

Chapter 22 – Pharmaceutical Side Effects / Allergic reactions to Pharmaceutical Drugs

Angie had been a patient in previous years. We did sporadic work on allergies and her elevated cholesterol levels. Well, that particular issue, elevated cholesterol, we never entirely resolved. Angie insisted on managing it with her natural supplements, like red rice yeast and other formulations. I tried to convince her to follow through with some functional epigenetic treatments. Cholesterol can be quite successfully balanced with the SHOW Method. In any case, a couple of years went by, I hadn't heard from Angie, until one Monday morning we got a call from Angie. She had had a heart attack this past weekend and had a stint inserted in one of her coronary arteries over the weekend. Apparently one of the coronaries was occluded 90%. She reported instant relief from the devastating chest constriction, right arm pain and breathing difficulties she had experienced leading up to that weekend. BUT she was crying, she needed help, she was reporting a severe UTI (Urinary tract infection) and she was scared of antibiotics. They make her feel awful.

Angie came into the clinic the next day. Indeed, she was in the bathroom every 5 minutes. But not much coming out. She was beside herself.

I started to check her out. Neither the computer scan nor my kinesiology testing (MRT) pointed towards an infection. No bacteria in sight.

I asked her about her meds. Well, she had been put on 3 medications: a blood thinner, a statin drug and a baby aspirin. She had all 3 meds in her purse.

I tested the medications on her body and low and behold, she was allergic to the blood thinner. Some fairly new and phantastic variety of blood thinner. It's called Brilinta®. She reacted allergic to it, or adverse in the energetic testing. So, what can we do? I couldn't very well suggest skipping the drug. Her stint was only 3 or 4 days old, so she needed to continue that medication.

We had to desensitize Angie to the Blood Thinner medication. That simple. No other reasonable option in the real world. So, no hesitation on my part. A little convincing to the patient, because she expected a classic UTI, which is usually bacterial. But it was the Brilinta® that caused the symptoms of a severe

UTI. I used one tablet from her pill bottle as well as a custom-made digital copy I created of the medication and I put together the following SHOW Method treatment:

- **Brilinta®** - in combination with Acid, Base, Organs, Hypothalamus and Interleukin 1 beta

---

IL-1β – is a cytokine and an important mediator of the inflammatory response, and is involved in a variety of cellular activities, including cell proliferation, differentiation, and apoptosis.

I also prescribed a Probiotic, because that's what her body asked for.

The next morning, I called Angie. I had been worrying all night, I hope I did this right, I pray this treatment will have the anticipated result. I hope it wasn't a bacterial UTI (which I could not find).

Angie answered the phone, and I asked, "How is your UTI". She was quite happy and declared; "3 hours after my appointment the UTI symptoms and discomfort were gone. Thank you so much".

Relief. We did it. The stars were aligned favorably.

We did do a second treatment on her follow-up visit. Because life goes on and we always try to prevent events like these from occurring. The follow-up treatment was a reinforcement, sometimes we call it a booster, of IL-1 beta. This time with some other important components in the Fatty Acids category.

- **IL – 1β, IL-16, Vitamin F, Essential Fatty Acids**

Now, just a routine treatment to continue supporting Angie's body to express the many biochemical details of life as best as possible. Supporting her Innate Intelligence in operating her life. And, of course to assist her body to heal the present crisis and medical intervention.

This wasn't the first time I had to treat someone for a lifesaving medication. In fact, we have done many such treatments. From Thyroid Hormone meds to analgesics like Lidocaine. And I remain surprised at how quickly and how successfully these treatments work.

You may ask, well, how do these treatments work? What actually happens.

I believe we are activating epigenetic pathways which detoxify these pharmaceutical chemicals properly, so there are no adverse effects any longer. So called adverse events to medications are detoxification difficulties, which can also manifest as allergies. And these kind of 'problems 'respond just magically to the epigenetic harmonization treatments of the SHOW Method and ASR Biofeedback (App 16).

"Life is and will ever remain an equation incapable of solution, but it contains certain known factors." *- Nikola Tesla*

Chapter 23 - Frozen Shoulder

Shoulders are an amazing and complex joint. Did you know that the only synovial articulation between your arms and the rest of the skeleton (trunk) is the AC joint?

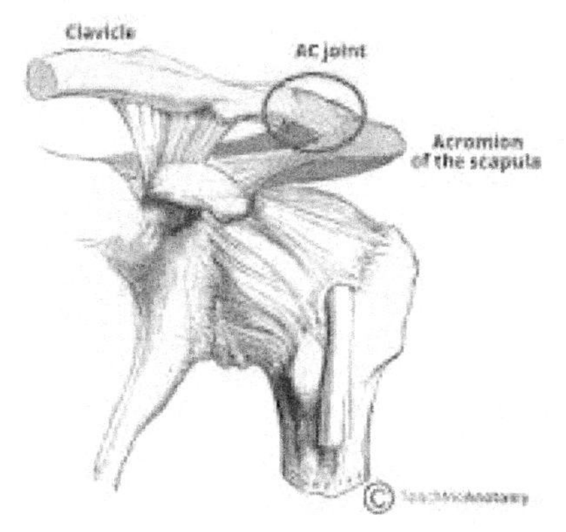

The acromioclavicular (AC) joint is the junction between the acromion (part of the scapula that forms the highest point of the shoulder) and the clavicle. It is a plane synovial joint.

All other attachments of the arms and shoulder with the main body are ligaments, cartilage and muscles. Most famously the rotator cuff muscles, a set of more than 6 muscles, affecting movement of the upper arm and stabilizing the shoulder.

Frozen shoulder is a fairly common phenomena and the solutions are not very convincing. Nothing really works very well therapeutically. The Mayo clinic says, usually within 1 to 3 years it will go away on its own.

Could it really be self-limiting? A virus or something like it.

One of the most common causes I found over the years with my patients, is a chronic Bartonella infection. Or, to put it into lay terms, a presence of Bartonella. There are no good test out there to confirm or identify Bartonella. Nor are there good answers on how to get rid of it. Anti-biotics don't work. So, we are back to where we started in the beginning of this book – our own Immune System has to do the job. And, **it can**.

This is Vicky's amazing (but not uncommon) frozen shoulder story. One of the more fascinating angles to Vicky's frozen shoulder is, that her older sister had this condition for years, earlier. It did not self-correct and her doctors suggested and did a shoulder replacement surgery. Unfortunately, this did not resolve her pain issues in the shoulder, and she is living with the pain now.

Back to Vicky, who pursued an alternative, Holistic Energy Medicine employing the SHOW Method.

Vicky presented with white spots on her forearms, severely decreased ROM of the left shoulder and pain. She could not reach for a plate in the cupboard or lift her arm even beyond her elbow height. She was actually in 3 years earlier complaining about shoulder pain, but we never got past 2 treatments, mainly chiropractic, because I also thought this was a physical problem and we were going to resolve it with physical modalities.

This time, we got to work with a series of 10 SHOW Method treatments:

- **Vitamin C** and **Common Flu Virus**
- **Animal Fats**
- **Vitamin A, DPT vaccine and Rubella**
- **Sugars** and **Pollen**
- **Grains** and **Gluten**
- **Wheat** and **Grass**
- **Vitamin B Complex**
- **Legumes** and **common Staph/Strep**
- **Dairy** and **Calcium**
- **Yeast** and **Candida**

The white spots had gone away by now.

We struggled with the shoulder. I did chiropractic to the neck and upper thoracic vertebra, ultrasound treatments, tried myofascial release, but too painful. Many other modalities to no avail.

We continued with the SHOW Method:

- **Vegetable Fats, NCR** (Nuclear Cytokine receptor)
- **Iron, Vitamin B 12, FUT2**
- **Salt**

*Cytoplasmic and **nuclear cytokine receptor** complexes. ...*
*The signaling from the plasma membrane activated **cytokine receptor** is driven to the cell nucleus by a rapid ricochet of protein phosphorylation, ultimately integrated as a differentiative, proliferative, or transcriptional message.*
(Interleukins are a group of cytokines)

With every EHT (SHOW Method/ASR Biofeedback), we also did some manual modality (Chiropractic & Myofascial release) in an effort to get the shoulder moving and reduce the pain. But, besides occasional temporary improvements, the lack of ROM now spread to the right shoulder. It started becoming very stiff.

Vicky did not give up. We continued:

- **Wheat, Gliadin, HLA DQ2 gene**
- **Tree Nuts**
- **Common Molds**

Today Vicky reports a head cold and she is very stuffy. Her treatment:

- **Flu Viruses**

Remember, we treated her for flu viruses on the first treatment. Definitely a susceptibility there.

- **Phenols** and **PBB**

Vicky reported as a child being exposed to PBB (Polybrominated biphenyls) in her neighborhood in Michigan. We determined some medicinal detox support and moved on.

- **Nightshade vegetable**
- **Shellfish**

The Ileocecal valve was determined 'stuck open' multiple times during this year of treatments and we manually closed it several times.

The shoulders were still bad. Now the right shoulder had become worse than the left. But Vicky did not give up. She could feel changes all through her body. She could feel that we were working on some 'old' stuff. Mostly she could feel it in her upper abdominal area and organs.

- **Vitamin E** and **SOX10 gene**
- **Bac 104** and **CYP7A1 gene**

Suddenly Lyme showed up. Apparently, there are other family members, including the older sister, who have had bouts with Lyme. We treated it 3 times:

- **Borrelia burgdorferi**
- **Borrelia burgdorferi**
- **Borrelia burgdorferi**

We employed Colostrum to support the Immune effort to eliminate (chronic) Lyme.

- **Borrelia burgdorferi**
- **Borrelia burgdorferi**

We did Borrelia/Lyme 5 times over a month's period, and, here shows up Bartonella for the first time. We had strengthened the metabolism significantly, cleared out multiple chronic infections, so, Vicky's system was ready to tackle Bartonella:

- **Bartonella** and **Yeast**
- **Lyme** and **Iodine**
- **Bartonella, Vitamin C** and **Citrus**
- **Vitamin B6** and **GTPase gene**
- **Bartonella** and **GTPase gene**
- **Bartonella, Lyme** and **IL-4**
- **Bartonella** and **feathers**
- **Bac 104** and **TGF beta**
- **Borrelia burgdorferi**
- **Borrelia burgdorferi** and **Animal dander**
- **Bartonella** and **TGF beta gene**

While we're working away at 1 or 2 treatments a week, the ROM of the shoulders started to improve. Finally. I had given up on other modalities, except chiropractic to the neck and upper thoracic spine. Now, Vicky was encouraged. It all came together. She continued:

- **Dust**
- **Bartonella** and **HLA 2Q8**
- **Epstein Barr Virus** and **IL-5**
- **Bartonella** and **IL-5**
- **Bartonella** and **DRD4 gene**

Both shoulders softened up. The ROM came back quickly now, without any additional mechanistic modalities.

So, what happened?!

Well, you be the judge. On the internet they say there's nothing you can do; it will resolve eventually on its own. And indeed, we worked on this particular case a full year. So, was it time, or the treatments?

Vicky knows. She's not naïve. Her frequent colds are long gone. Her intestinal issues are no more. The skin issue, which brought her in initially, cleared up rather quickly and early on.

Vicky has family members, who serve as a sort of a control group. Several have the same physical symptoms, for years, and their general state of health is rather compromised.

Vicky enjoys full ROM of both of her shoulders. She has no more pain anywhere and she enjoys vibrant health. Her Immune System appears iron clad.

I now routinely check for Lyme and Bartonella with every case of Frozen Shoulder coming into our clinic. And guess what, it's a thing. It's a phenomenon. Especially Bartonella seems to be present in almost every case.

I'll just keep listening to the body and ask the appropriate questions (and electronically scan). The body holds all the answers. It's just a matter of deciphering the body's energy and learning the language to communicate with the Innate, the DNA and associated divine structures.

" When one encounters muddled circumstance and uncertainty don't try and stir the dirt out, but leave it alone that the mud may settle, and then see with clarity."

- Lao Tzu

Chapter 24 - Pink Shade # 1001 – Summary

Health is just not as simple as numbers in blood work or a picture from a MRI etc. These physical measures can establish many pathologies. Which people with pathologies often need. I get asked all the time: "Doctor, can you tell me what's wrong with me, nobody can figure it out or nobody's diagnosis seems to be the right answer." Unfortunately, I must reply, "NO, I can't tell you what's wrong." When I feel brave enough, I say: "I don't have a clue what's wrong with you." The fact is, it's many things, it's thousands of mutations and many infections and once we get started working on these "quirks" and genetic imperfections a picture will emerge of what this is all about and we will be able to harmonize your function one step at the time and to various degrees.

Some recoveries are miraculous and quick, some are a lot of work and go on for years. After all, this is what healthcare is supposed to be; preventing people from developing pathologies. Not just saying, oh your blood pressure is a bit too high, here is a pill to keep it in range. Never mind what's causing it and never mind identifying those things which are responsible for the deficit and trying to 'heal' them. However, that's exactly what the SHOW Method is attempting to do and facilitate.

My 'favorite' frequent response from the medical establishment to so many health issues; be it scoliosis, HPV infection or even chronic bronchitis, is: 'we'll watch it and when it gets to the point where you need intervention, we'll let you know. In the meantime, here is a prescription to manage your discomfort or the numbers'. The problem with this approach is that the underlying disease process continues.

For this type of precision healing and on prevention focused Energy Medicine, the two biggest factors are AGE and severity of the mutations. The younger the individual, the better the health outcome, the faster the results, the easier the treatment protocol, the greater the lifelong benefits. The second factor is that there are different stages and severity of mutations: SNPs are the most common ones. We all have thousands of those. But even with SNPs, there are heterozygous ones (single rung of the ladder = one parent heritance) and homozygous ones (both rungs = both parent's heritance). Heterozygous heredity equals approximately a 30% dysfunction, homozygous heredity equals up to 90% dysfunction.

These mutations are related to allergies of all kinds, sensitivities, difficulties to detoxify, mental issues and the treatments of those issues are highly successful. On the other hand, severe mutations of entire sections of a chromosome, such as Cystic Fibrosis, are much more difficult to work with and need to be prevented altogether!

Nevertheless, since this kind of precision energy treatments are epigenetic, they are also heritable. So, couples or mothers who intend to become pregnant or are pregnant; they are to benefit the most from going through a set of these treatments and taking care of their allergies and infectious stressors. Just one small example would be the notion to PREVENT Autism. (App 9)

The same is true for cancer. Many cancers are caused by chronic viral infections. Vaccinations will not be the answer. There are too many viruses to worry about. (There are over 120 HPV varieties alone). Finding the viruses and getting the Immune System to eliminate those viruses is the answer.

The same is true for Alzheimer's. An avalanche of over 3 million new diagnosis every year. Even the pharmaceutical industry this year publicly announced that it will not spend any more money on the cure of Alzheimer's, because there will be no cure possible any time soon. Instead, Alzheimer's must be prevented, and they will spend their research dollars on developing medications to prevent Alzheimer's. You don't have to wait for that train to leave the station either. It's obvious that Alzheimer's must be prevented, and it starts in childhood. I have shown a path on how to prevent Alzheimer's in previous papers. (APP 12)

Yes, the cycle of passing allergies and genetic predispositions on to the next generation can be broken. The effect of these kind of energy treatments appear very much to be heritable.

For the older people amongst us. Well, it's the DNA that ages, that's how we age, telomeres and all! The SHOW Method is the most advanced anti-aging strategy around (next to healthy lifestyle choices). So yes, it takes a little more effort to harmonize aging genes, then young genes. But they are no less, very much able to resonate to frequencies and harmonize themselves. The biggest challenge with older folks is to rehabilitate the tissues which have been damaged by a lifetime of inflammation. That's where natural medicines come in very handy. Natural medicines nurture the body's tissues, while pharmaceuticals are chemicals which must be detoxified. And as I described in previous chapters, many people have SNPs and mutations in their detoxification cycle genes. Pharmaceuticals, just like other toxins damage the DNA (to different degrees) and cause further genetic damage. Besides bad dietary habits and a toxic agriculture sector, our present healthcare system is a main contributor to the decline of our children's health. It all results in a declining genome. A frightening thought.

Much work needs to be done. Epigenetics are complex and ever changing. You can join our efforts of bringing this concept to the mainstream of healthcare through your support of our 501 (c)(3) SmartHealth Inc. www.smarthealth4u.org (App 10)

You can find a SHOW Method practitioner near you on the IMAET website, www.imaet.com. (App 11)

Appendix-A: Basic Allergen Chart-SHOW Method

Chart – Basic Allergens – SHOW Method

1. MBB______________________________
2. Vitamin B Complex________________________
3. Eggs/Chicken__________________________
4. Candida/Yeast_________________________
5. Sugars_____________________________
6. Grains_____________________________
7. Dairy/Milk___________________________
8. Gluten_____________________________
9. Peanuts____________________________
10. Tree Nuts___________________________
11. Vitamin C___________________________
12. Vitamin A___________________________
13. Vitamin D___________________________
14. Vitamin E___________________________
15. Vitamin K___________________________
16. Soy/Beans___________________________
17. Wheat/Gliadin_________________________
18. Calcium____________________________
19. Iron______________________________
20. Iodine_____________________________
21. Minerals____________________________
22. Veg/Anim Fats_________________________
23. Shellfish____________________________
24. Spices/Phenols________________________
25. Tree Pollen__________________________
26. Spring Pollen_________________________
27. Grasses____________________________
28. Weeds/Hayfever_______________________
29. Basic Molds__________________________
30. Nightshade Veg/peppers__________________
31. Dog/Cat Hair__________________________
32. Dust______________________________
33. Perfumes___________________________
34. Formaldehyde_________________________
35. Herbicides/Pesti_______________________
36. Cold/Flu Viruses_______________________

Appendix/References:

1) http://www.smarthealth4u.org/index.php/show-method
2) www.NAET.com
3) www.imaet.com
4) http://www.ncbi.nlm.nih.gov/pubmed/16022630
5) www.standardprocess.com
6) info on product AF-Betafood (www.standard process.com)
7) https://www.youtube.com/watch?v=r3cqJMFN7ls
8) You 1, Anxiety 0 – Jodi Aman. www.Givefeartheboot.com
9) http://docstraile.com/auto-immune/autism-prevent-now/
10) www.smarthealth4u.org
11) www.imaet.com/index.php/en/find-a-practitioner
12) http://docstraile.com/alzheimers/alzheimers-prevent-now/
13) NCBI (National Center for Biotechnology) APMIS Suppl 2013 May (136);1-51. Bjarnsholt: The role of biofilms in chronic infections.
14) Brown (Juice) – WEI Laboratories. www.weilab.com
15) Bioactive products found in onion: read more at www.sigmaaldrich.com/life-science/nutrition-research/learning
16) ASR Biofeedback Blog Dr. Straile at www.smarthealth4u.org/blog

Notes

Notes

Notes

Made in the USA
Monee, IL
13 November 2020